MEDICINE THROUGH TIME

FOR THE SCHOOLS HISTORY PROJECT

NEW EDITION

Joe Scott
Christopher Culpin

General Editor of original edition: Ian Dawson

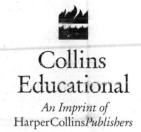

Collins
Educational
An Imprint of
HarperCollins*Publishers*

Contents

How to Use This Book

Have you ever broken your leg? Did you have to have an operation? What would have happened if you lived in prehistoric times and broke a leg? Suppose you lived in Ancient Rome or Victorian Britain: what could be done for you?

In the first part of this book, called **The Story in Outline**, you will find out the answers to these and all sorts of other questions about the history of medicine. There are key questions (marked ◆) to tell you what each section is about and other questions (marked ❖) to get you thinking. There are lots of historical sources because that is how historians find out about the past.

Look again at the picture. Why are the surgeons wearing masks? What are the tools in the front for and why are they designed like that? What are the machines in the background doing? How do the surgeons know what to do? All kinds of medical ideas have come together to make this operation successful. How, why and when were all these discoveries made?

Historians are not just interested in *what* happened, they want to know *why*. In the second part of this book, called **Issues and Enquiries,** you will first look at four of the factors which helped to cause change at several points in the history of medicine. Then you will look again at the whole story, asking questions about the patterns of change like ' Have things got steadily better?' You will often look back to **The Story in Outline** to remind yourself what happened.

You may be using this book to prepare for your GCSE examination. You will find that it has summaries and timelines to help you to revise. It has sections called **Examining the Evidence** to give you some practice at Paper 2. Most of all, though, we hope you enjoy finding out how important the past is in helping us all understand the present.

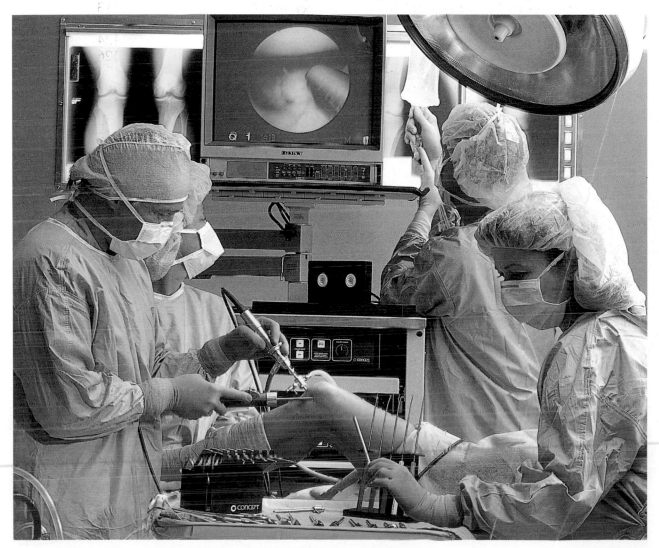

MEDICINE THROUGH TIME

Health has always been a basic human need. Today, as at every earlier period, people need to know how to care for mothers in pregnancy and childbirth and for young children as they grow up. They need to know how to live a healthy life and how to deal with accidents like broken bones. They need to know how to help and reassure the sick and to prevent or cure diseases. They need to know how to look after the old and the dying.

Medicine Through Time is the story of how people tackled these problems, and how new methods and ideas for dealing with them developed and spread from one area of the world to another.

Look at the two stories told in pictures on these two pages. They are both really the same.
❖ *What is happening in each picture?*
❖ *What do you think the people in each story are saying and thinking?*

Stone Age Medicine

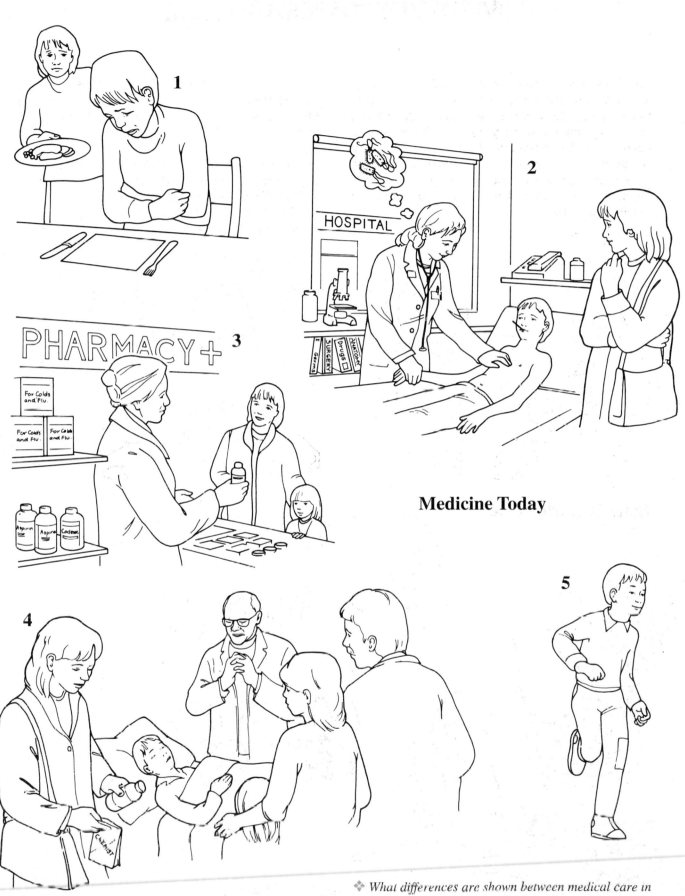

Medicine Today

❖ *What differences are shown between medical care in prehistoric times and today?*

❖ *What aspects of medical care have stayed the same?*

❖ *What other aspects of medical care, not shown here, are different or have stayed the same over time?*

MEDICINE IN PREHISTORIC TIMES

KEY QUESTIONS
- ◆ *What medical knowledge did prehistoric people have?*
- ◆ *What medical treatments did they carry out?*
- ◆ *How can we find out about medicine in prehistoric times?*

Health mattered a lot to prehistoric people. At first they lived by hunting and gathering food, so they had to move about often. Even when they settled in one place as farmers they had to work hard or starve to death. So sick people and people who had been injured had to get fit again as soon as possible. If enough children were not born and cared for, the group would die out. Health was really important.

Evidence from prehistoric times

We know almost nothing about prehistoric medical care. We can only go on the evidence that has survived. Very little of it tells us about medicine.

SOURCE 1

Skilful carving of a reindeer antler c. 1200 BC. It shows a bison turning its head to lick its side.

Prehistoric people were careful observers of nature. They were also skilled craftsmen, as we can tell from objects like Source 1. Did they apply their skill and care to medicine? Fortunately they did leave behind them one type of evidence of medical skill. At many prehistoric sites archaeologists have found skulls like the ones in Source 2, in which holes have been carefully made. This is known as trephining.

At first archaeologists thought that the holes had been cut to let the dead person's spirit get out. But later many skulls were found in which the bone round the hole had grown smooth and round – the person had survived the operation!

SOURCE 2

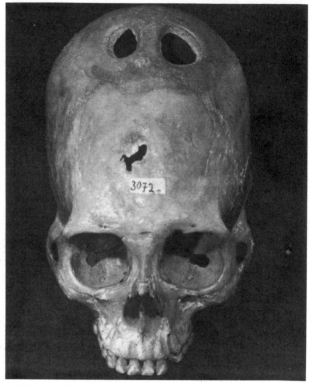

Prehistoric skull.

- ❖ *Who cut the holes, and why did they cut them?*
- ❖ *The bone around these holes is smooth and rounded. What can we tell from this?*
- ❖ *Why might prehistoric people have carried out this dangerous and difficult operation?*

6

Evidence from more recent times

In many parts of the world a way of life similar to that of prehistoric people has continued until recent times. Perhaps clues to the medical ideas of prehistoric people can be found by studying groups who still live as hunter-gatherers or semi-nomadic farmers. These groups differ greatly from each other, but one feature is common to all: their explanations of many natural events are based on belief in spirits.

These invisible spirits are everywhere, and they are very powerful. There are good and bad spirits and they affect everyday activities of all kinds. People and animals have their own spirits. A run of bad luck or sudden illness may be explained by the action of the spirits.

Some modern Australian aborigines, for instance, believe that there are evil spirits which live in holes in gum trees. At night these spirits wander around, and if they enter the bodies of sleeping people they can cause sickness or death.

The obvious cure for sickness caused in this way is to deal with the evil spirit. The medicine man sings the sick person into a trance, massaging the sore part of the body and sucking it hard. Then he produces from his hand a quartz crystal into which the evil spirit has moved. The patient often recovers.

❖ *How might ideas like this about the cause of disease help to explain trephining?*
❖ *Does this prove that prehistoric people must have had similar ideas?*
❖ *Sometimes a treatment like that shown in Source 4 did not work, but the aborigines went on using it. Why would they do this?*

SOURCE 3

By pointing a bone like this and chanting, the Australian medicine man makes an evil spirit enter a person's body or entices the person's own spirit away. From a photograph.

SOURCE 4
An Australian medicine man massaging a sick man with sweat from his own armpits. Modern photograph.

Medicine without magic

Some common medical problems, like cuts or broken limbs, could be dealt with more directly. The Australian aborigines have practical methods of dealing with these things. Here are some of the remedies they use:

- Open cuts are covered with a pad of mud, paper bark and kangaroo skin.
- Stomach disorders are treated by chewing young shoots of certain plants or an orchid bulb.
- Broken arms are encased in mud and clay.

Other people living a nomadic way of life in recent times knew of similar remedies and useful medicinal herbs. 'Squaw Root' for instance is a root whose juice affects the uterus. It was used by native North Americans to help towards a quick and easy labour. The leaves of the coca plant were chewed by South American Indians and the juice was smeared on injured parts of the body to kill pain. The modern anaesthetic cocaine is made from these leaves.

❖ *How might the recent people who used remedies of this sort have learned about them?*
❖ *Does this help us to decide whether prehistoric people used this sort of remedy?*

Medicine men

Many prehistoric people lived in small groups, little larger than a single family. They probably relied on the wisdom and knowledge of parents and grandparents. But sometimes when hunting was good and food was plentiful people were able to live together in larger groups. Often there was a leading member of the group with specific knowledge and authority. Such a person might have a wide knowledge of practical remedies or great skill in dealing with the spirits.

These 'medicine men' could not read or write, so they would hand down their wisdom and knowledge in songs, stories and dances.

❖ *How might this method of teaching help in the development of medical knowledge?*
❖ *Do the trephined skulls help us to decide whether prehistoric people had specially skilled medicine men?*
❖ *Prehistoric people had two kinds of remedy – practical treatments and magic. Which was more powerful and important to them?*

SOURCE 1
Cave painting from France, c. 15 000 BC. Could this show a medicine man dancing a ritual dance?

SOURCE 2

American Indian medicine man. (Drawn in 1841)

SOURCE 3 – Death by magic

A person who knows that he is the object of witchcraft is thoroughly convinced that he is doomed. His friends and relatives share his certainty. From then on the community withdraws. It treats him as a source of danger to the whole group. Sacred rites are held to send him to the land of shadows. The victim yields to the effect of intense terror . . . (and dies).

C. Levi-Strauss, *Structural Anthropology*. An anthropologist studies human customs and traditional behaviour.

❖ *Can medicine men be called the first doctors?*

MEDICINE IN THE FIRST CIVILISATIONS

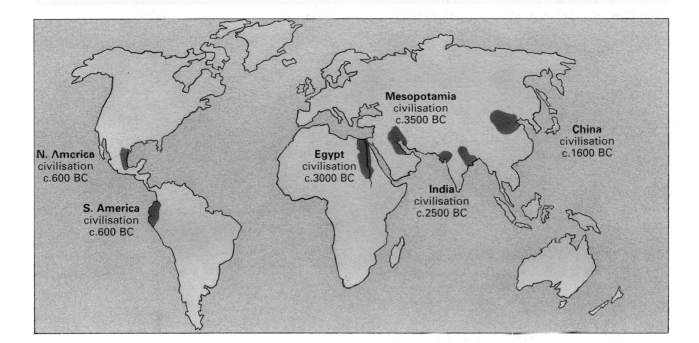

The first cities developed in Mesopotamia about 3500 BC. During the next 3000 years others grew up in other areas, as shown on the map. Many developments took place. How might the developments shown below affect medicine?

In the fertile areas where these civilisations developed, large numbers of people were able to stay permanently in the same place. The farmers could grow more than enough food for themselves, so they had a surplus to support specialist craftsmen. These in turn could develop new skills of many kinds, like writing or metal-working. People could build ships and trade with distant lands.

KEY QUESTION
◆ *Did old ideas continue in the first civilisations?*

SOURCE 1

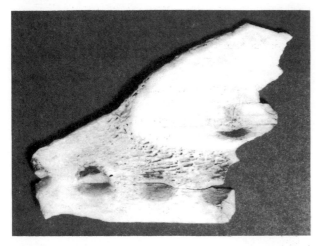

A Chinese oracle bone with the names of several diseases of various parts of the body written on it. A heated bronze point was placed against the bone, and from the cracks made by the heat the priest could tell what the spirits advised. Hundreds have been found dating from the Shang dynasty (14th–11th century BC).

SOURCE 2

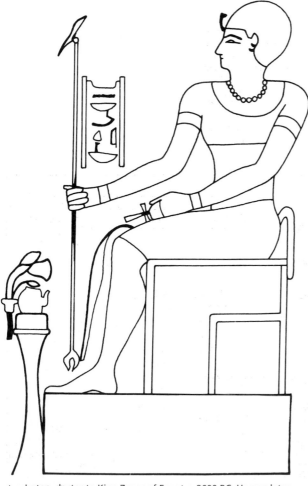

Imphotep, doctor to King Zozer of Egypt c. 2600 BC. He was later worshipped as a god of healing.

SOURCE 3

The funeral inscription of Irj, Pharaoh's doctor c. 1500 BC. It reads 'Palace doctor. Palace eye physician. Palace physician of the belly. Guardian of the anus.'

SOURCE 4

Doctor's seal from Lagash, Mesopotamia, 2000BC. The inscription reads 'O God Edinmugi, Servant of the God Gir, you who help animal mothers to give birth, Urlugaledina, the physician is thy servant.'

❖ *Did the early doctors still believe in spirits and the power of magic? The sources on this page will help you to answer this question.*
❖ *What else do these sources tell you about early medical methods and knowledge?*
❖ *What do these sources tell you about the way medical knowledge was passed on?*

SOURCE 5

This prescription written in Sumeria about 2100 BC says 'Crush to powder the seeds of carpenter's herb and the gummy resin of thyme. Dissolve in beer and give to the man to drink.' It does not say what the treatment was for.

SOURCE 7 – Spell to be said while drinking a remedy

Here is the great remedy. Come! You who drive evil things from my stomach and my limbs. He who drinks this shall be cured just as the gods above were cured. This spell is really excellent – successful many times!

Ebers Papyrus, Egypt c. 1500 BC

SOURCE 8 – A spell and a healing plant

O Takman, god of the fiery element, feel with us and spare us. I pay honour to the cold Takman and to the hot. Honour be to Takman who returns on the next day.

Kushta, the most healing of plants, you are born in the mountains. Come down, O Kushta, destroy Takman, drive Takman away from here. Aches in the head, inflammation on the eye, pains in the body – all these Kushta plant heals.

The *Atharvaveda*, an Indian medical book based on tradition going back to c. 1000 BC, but written down later. The disease is probably malaria, which makes people first sweat and then shiver.

SOURCE 6

Part of an Egyptian medical book, discovered in 1862. It was written about 1550 BC, but in part was copied from earlier documents. Much of our knowledge of early Egyptian medicine is based on a group of books like this. They were written on papyrus, a paper made from reeds.

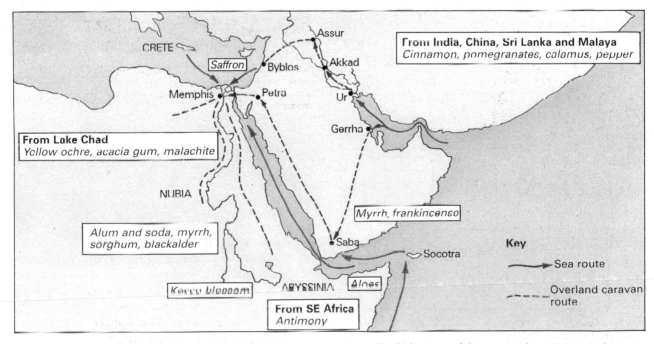

SOURCE 9

Routes by which spices and drugs were taken to Egypt. We have evidence from the written records that the doctors of each of the early civilisations knew of several hundred herbs.

Old ideas lead to new knowledge

Today we expect doctors to have a scientific understanding of how the body works. Before they can do this they have to understand anatomy, the structure of the body. This can only be learned properly by the careful dissection of dead bodies.

How important was a knowledge of anatomy for the doctors in the early civilisations? How easy would it be for them to learn about the structure of the body? Before answering these questions remember that:

1. People still believed that diseases were mainly caused by spirits and gods.
2. People believed in a life after death. They would need their bodies in this after-life.
3. In one of the early civilisations, Egypt, important people were embalmed to prepare them for the after-life. This involved taking out parts of the body to stop them decaying. (See Source 1)

❖ *How would each of these things either hinder or help the growth of knowledge of anatomy?*

SOURCE 1

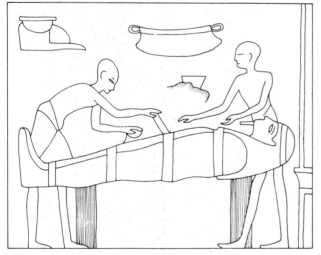

Painting from an Egyptian tomb showing embalmers at work, c. 500 BC.

SOURCE 2

Irrigation channels bringing water to farmland from the Nile. Life in Egypt depended on this system being kept in good order. How might this have led to the ideas in Source 3?

SOURCE 3 – Channels in the body for blood and other fluids

46 vessels go from the heart to every limb. If a doctor, priest of Sekhmet, or magician, places his hand or fingers on the back of the head, hands, stomach, arms or feet, then he hears the heart. The heart speaks out of every limb. There are four vessels in his nostrils, two give mucus and two give blood.

There are four vessels to his two ears. The breath of life enters into the right ear, and the breath of death enters into the left ear.

There are four vessels to the liver; it is they which give it fluid and air, which afterwards cause all diseases to arise in it by overfilling with blood.

There are four vessels to the lung and to the spleen. It is they which give fluid and air to it.

Ebers Papyrus, Egypt c. 1500 BC

❖ *What can we tell from this source about the Egyptian's knowledge of anatomy?*
❖ *How had they probably gained this knowledge?*
❖ *What can we tell from this source about new ideas on the cause of diseases?*

New techniques influence surgery

Knives of flint could be very sharp and effective, as the successful trephining operations of the Stone Age show. But the coming of metals, first bronze and then, about 1200 BC, iron and steel, gave the doctors much better surgical instruments.

SOURCE 4 – Cutting out a tumour

When you come across a swelling that has attacked a vessel, then it has formed a tumour in his body. If, when you examine it with your fingers, it is like a hard stone, then you should say, 'It is a tumour of the vessels. I shall treat the disease with a knife.

Ebers Papyrus, Egypt c. 1500 BC

SOURCE 5 – Operation on the eye

If a physician has opened a spot in a man's eye with a bronze instrument and so healed the man's eye, he is to be paid ten shekels of silver for his work.

If the doctor destroys the man's eye, his hands are to be cut off.

Laws of Hammurabi, Babylon c. 2000 BC

SOURCE 6

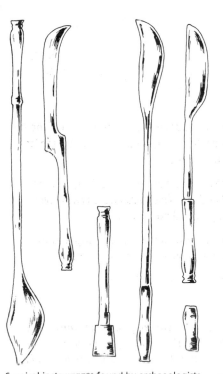

Surgical instruments found by archaeologists at Babylon. There are three knives, a saw and a trephining tool for cutting the skull.

In China the technique known as acupuncture was developed well before 1000 BC. Chinese doctors found that sharp pressure on certain points of the body had the effect of relieving pain. First they used sharp flints, but later silver or steel needles. They gradually built up a detailed knowledge of the points where the treatment worked best for patients with various complaints. It seems likely that the earliest Chinese doctors thought of it as a way of driving out evil spirits. Later, as you can read in the next section, they developed another theory.

SOURCE 7

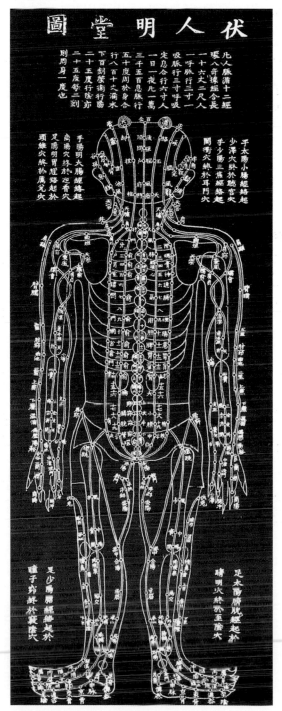

A 20th-century Chinese diagram of the acupuncture points of the human body.

Old and new ways of preventing disease

Just as there were two ways of treating illness – by magic or by practical treatments – so there were two ways of preventing illness. This could be done by keeping away the evil spirits, but also by practical commonsense methods.

SOURCE 1

Ancient Egyptian charm shaped like a beetle, which was thought to be very effective in frightening off evil spirits.

SOURCE 2a – Mosquito nets

Gnats are common, and this is how the Egyptians protect themselves against them. Each man has a net. By day it serves him to catch fish, while at night he spreads it over the bed. The gnats do not so much as attempt to pass the net.

SOURCE 2b – Egyptian priests wash twice a day

They drink from cups of bronze which they clean daily. They are specially careful to wear newly washed linen clothing. They practise circumcision for the sake of cleanliness. Their priests shave the whole body every third day so that no lice may infect them while they are in the service of the gods. Twice a day and every night they wash in cold water.

Herodotus *Histories*. Herodotus was a Greek who travelled in Egypt c. 450 BC and wrote his book soon afterwards. It was shown in AD 1898 that malaria is spread by mosquitoes and in 1916 that typhus is spread by lice.

SOURCE 3

An Egyptian lady making up. They used a green eye shadow made from malachite. This mineral can protect the eye from infection. From a drawing on papyrus.

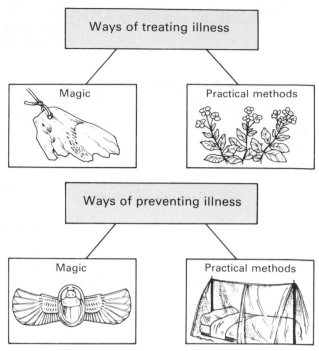

SOURCE 4

A public health system. Sewers at Mohenjo Daro, India c. 1500 BC. There were also water pipes and baths in this city of many thousands of people. As cities grew in size new health problems arose. How could the foul-smelling sewage of a crowded city be carried away? How could pure water be brought into the city? Modern scientists have shown how the germs of disease can be carried from sewage into the water supply.

❖ *People of the early civilisations did not know of the modern scientific explanations for the spread of diseases. How then could they have discovered these effective ways of preventing it?*

CHANGES AND DEVELOPMENTS BY 500 BC: SUMMARY

The drawings show some of the main changes that took place in medicine between prehistoric times and 500 BC, when the early civilisations were well established.

KEY QUESTIONS
- *What changes had taken place?*
- *What aspects of medicine had stayed the same?*
- *Why had things changed or stayed the same?*
- *Had these changes taken place quickly or slowly?*

Prehistoric times   **c. 500 BC**

1. Doctors and medical knowledge

2. Surgery and anatomy

3. Public health systems

4. The medicine of ordinary people

In 500 BC most people, even in advanced countries like Egypt or China, were still peasant farmers living in villages. Not many of them can often have consulted a trained doctor. In childbirth and in sickness they were cared for by their families and neighbours. The charms, herbs and common sense that they used were probably not very different from those used by prehistoric people.

MEDICINE IN THE ANCIENT WORLD, 500 BC – AD 500

KEY QUESTIONS
- ◆ *What did the Greeks learn about medicine from the civilisations of India, China, Mesopotamia and Egypt?*
- ◆ *How did the Greeks explain illness in a new, scientific way?*
- ◆ *How did the Romans try to keep healthy?*

The Greeks

During the thousand years from 500 BC to AD 500 people in all the civilised areas went on adding to medical knowledge. The area around the Mediterranean Sea became of special importance in this period. Here the Greeks produced many new ideas in art, government and science. Some of these were important for medicine.

In the 4th century BC, led by Alexander the Great, the Greeks conquered Egypt, Mesopotamia and part of India. In Egypt Alexander set up a new city, Alexandria. Here the Greeks started a university and a library where they collected together all the knowledge they could find, from India, Mesopotamia, Egypt and Greece. So Alexandria became a great centre for study, including the study of medicine.

The Romans

In the 2nd and 1st centuries BC the Romans conquered Greece and Egypt and made them parts of the Roman Empire, which stretched from Egypt to Britain. The Romans admired the Greeks and made great use of the knowledge they had collected. Most of the leading doctors in Rome were Greeks.

This period came to an end about 500 AD when the western part of the Roman Empire broke down and fell into disorder.

Mesopotamia   China

Egypt

India

Greeks collect ideas from many sources and add them to their own ideas

The Romans continue and spread Greek ideas

Time of Greek greatness | Rise of Roman Empire | Its decline and fall

| 500 | 400 | 356 323 | 300 | 200 | 100 | | 100 | 200 | 300 | 400 | 500 |

Life of Alexander

← BC   AD →

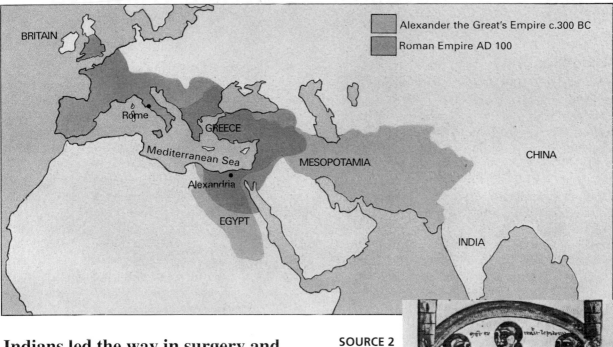

Indians led the way in surgery and anatomy

It seems likely that some of the new ideas that spread through the Greek and Roman world came first from India. Two Indian books, the *Charaka Samhita* and the *Susruta Samhita*, were probably written in their present form between about 200 BC and AD 200, though parts of them are much older.

SOURCE 1 – Dissecting a corpse

A perfectly preserved body must be used. It should be the body of a person who is not very old and did not die of poison or severe disease. After the intestines have been cleaned the body must be wrapped up and placed in a cage. The cage should be placed in a carefully concealed spot in a river, and the body left to soften. After seven days the body is removed from the water and with a brush it should be brushed off a layer at a time. When this is done, the eye can observe every part of the body, large or small, outer or inner. Beginning with the skin each part is laid bare by the brushing.

Susruta Samhita, India, before 200 AD

❖ *Can we conclude from this that the Indians dissected human bodies as a regular practice?*

The Indians who wrote these books obviously knew a lot of anatomy. Many of the major bones and muscles and organs were known. It is also clear from the books that the Indians had various theories about how the body worked. But their main achievement was in the practice of surgery. They were able to sew up cuts and operation wounds, to remove a cataract from the eye, to repair a damaged nose by plastic surgery, and even to remove a stone from the bladder.

SOURCE 2

An operation to remove a stone from the bladder (14th-century European drawing). This is the earliest picture, but the operation was known in India in ancient times.

SOURCE 3

An 18th-century European drawing showing how the Indians repaired a nose with a skin graft. This operation was known in India in ancient times.

THE BEGINNINGS OF SCIENTIFIC THINKING

New explanations

At about the same time as the Indians were making advances in surgery, some doctors in Greece and in China were thinking in a new way about the causes of disease. They were looking for a new kind of explanation.

Before about 500 BC most people had been content with the old supernatural explanations – Gods and spirits controlled the earth and caused events like storms or diseases.

Now some thinkers suggested that the world worked according to a natural system which human beings might understand. If they could, then natural explanations would take the place of supernatural ones. This was an idea of very great importance. The whole of modern science is based upon it.

Greek and Chinese thinkers put forward natural explanations for many things from the movement of the planets to the behaviour of animals. Once people applied the same sort of thinking to medicine, they began to come up with natural explanations of the causes of disease.

SOURCE 1 – Doctors are not magicians

My own view is that those who first called this disease (epilepsy) sacred were like the magicians or quacks of our own day. The disease called sacred comes from the same causes as others. So there is no need to put this disease in a special class or to consider it more divine than the others. Each disease has a nature and power of its own: none is hopeless or incapable of treatment. So the doctor can give useful treatment without using any magic.

Hippocrates, *The Sacred Disease*, Greece c. 400 BC.

SOURCE 2 – Look for symptoms – not ghosts

In treating illness you should look at all the circumstances, look carefully at the symptoms, observe the conditions and attitudes (of the patient). If you speak of the presence of ghosts and spirits you cannot speak of medical treatment.

The Yellow Emperor's *Manual of Medicine*, China between 450 and 350 BC.

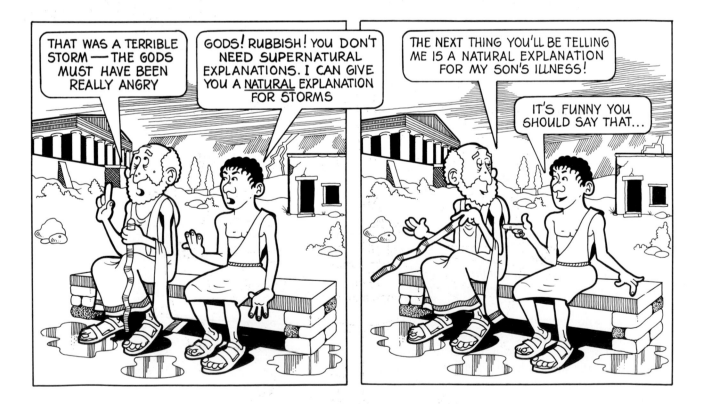

There were three theories about the natural causes of disease in the ancient world:
1. The Chinese theory of Yin and Yang
2. Astrology
3. The Greek theory of the four humours.

New theories
1. The Chinese theory of Yin and Yang

The Chinese thinkers saw two main sorts of energy, Yin and Yang, in everything, including all human beings. Yin and Yang are opposites. They are linked to darkness and light, female and male, cold and hot, death and life, winter and summer. A healthy person needed a proper balance of the two. By examining the patient carefully a doctor could find what was wrong. He could then recommend acupuncture to control the flow of energy in the body, or herbs or other treatment to restore the balance.

SOURCE 3 – Yang and Yin

On the outside of the body there is Yang, and inside there is Yin. The liver, heart, spleen, lungs and kidneys are Yin, and the five hollow organs, gall-bladder, stomach, lower intestines and bladder, are all Yang. The diseases of spring are located within the Yin areas of the body, and the diseases of autumn in the Yang areas. We must know the locations of these diseases for the purpose of acupuncture.

The Yellow Emperor's *Manual of Medicine*, China, between 450 and 350 BC.

2. Astrology – the influence of the stars

The idea that heavenly bodies like the sun, the moon and the stars affected people's lives was very old. The Chinese and the Babylonians had developed this idea, but it was the Greeks who worked it out in most detail. Greek astronomers thought that the Earth was in the centre of the universe, and that the heavenly bodies circled round it, sending down their influences on it. People knew that these influences were connected with changes like the seasons and the tides. The Greeks worked out a complex theory of how the planets and the stars affected individual people and various parts of their bodies at certain particular times.

SOURCE 4

An English astrological book, late 14th or early 15th century, showing how the signs of the zodiac were thought to influence parts of the body. This idea was first developed by the Greeks in Alexandria.

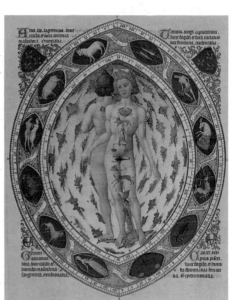

SOURCE 5

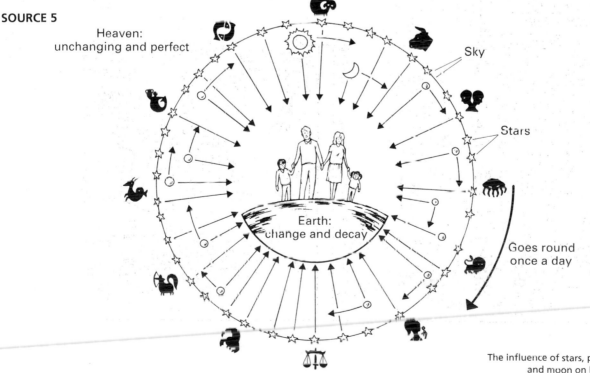

Heaven: unchanging and perfect

Sky

Stars

Earth: change and decay

Goes round once a day

The influence of stars, planets, sun and moon on human life.

3. The Greek theory of the four humours

This theory was that there were four main fluids or humours in the body – blood, phlegm, yellow bile and black bile.

SOURCE 1 – The humours and health

When all these humours are truly balanced a person feels the most perfect health. Illness happens when there is too much of one humour or too little or it is entirely thrown out of the body.

Hippocrates, *On the constitution of man*, Greece, c. 400 BC.

The weather or other factors, such as getting too wet or eating the wrong foods, could unbalance the humours and cause illness. This fitted in very neatly with the Greek idea of the four elements. Everything, they thought, was a mixture of four basic elements: earth, air, fire and water. They were linked with the four seasons of the year as well as with the four humours in the human body, as the diagram shows. For instance in winter people have many colds and this was because they had too much phlegm.

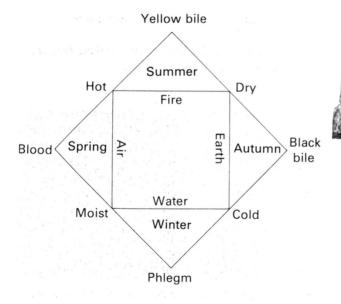

SOURCE 2

Tombstone of the Athenian doctor, Jason. The object on the right is a bleeding cup, shown larger than it really was. It was heated and placed over a small scratch made in the patient's back. Then it was cooled and this sucked out blood into the vacuum.

SOURCE 3

If the pain is under the diaphragm, clear the bowels with a medicine made from black hellebore, cumin or other fragrant herbs. A bath will help pneumonia as it soothes the pain and brings up phlegm. But the bather must be quiet. He must do nothing himself but leave the pouring of water and rubbing to others.

Hippocratic writings, *On the treatment for acute diseases*, Greece 400–200 BC.

❖ *Did the theory of the four humours play any part in this treatment?*

Treatments based on the theory

By a careful examination of the patient, for instance by looking at his or her urine, a doctor could tell how the humours were unbalanced. As in the Chinese system, the doctor's task was then to help nature to restore the proper balance. A patient might be made to vomit to remove the bile, or might be heated or cooled. The most drastic treatment was bleeding to draw off an excess of blood, so as to restore the balance of the humours.

Hippocrates

Hippocrates was the most famous Greek doctor. He was born on the island of Cos about 460 BC, just when the new idea of natural causes was being accepted in the Greek world. We have later copies of about sixty medical books said to be by Hippocrates, although most of them were probably written over the next two or three hundred years by his followers. This does not affect their value as evidence for Greek medical ideas at this time.

Hippocrates

Clinical observation

('Clinical' comes from a Greek word meaning 'bedside'.)

Hippocrates and his followers insisted on the importance of carefully observing patients and recording their symptoms. They took over much knowledge of these symptoms from the Egyptians. What was new was the Greek idea that sickness was something natural that ran its own natural course. By recording 'case histories' the doctor could learn what this natural course was. Once he could forecast how it would develop he could apply the correct treatment just as the disease reached the right point – they knew that many patients recovered naturally so they often did nothing but advise rest, exercise and proper food.

SOURCE 4 – A Greek case history

Silenus began with pains in his abdomen, heavy head and stiff neck.
First day: he vomited, his urine was black, he was thirsty, tongue dry, no sleep at night.
Second day: slightly delirious.
Sixth day: slight perspiration about the head, head and feet cold, no discharge from the bowels, no urine.
Eighth day: cold sweat all over, red rashes, severe diarrhoea.
Eleventh day: he died – breathing slow and heavy. His age was about twenty.

From one of the Hippocratic books, *On Epidemics*.

Old medical ideas continue

The coming of new ideas never means that everybody suddenly scraps the old ones. A good example of this is the belief of the Greeks in supernatural cures. The Greeks had many gods, and one of these, Asklepios, had been worshipped as a god of healing since early times. Long after the time of Hippocrates many Greeks went on believing that illness could be cured by the gods. Temples of Asklepios continued to be built and used throughout Greek and Roman times. Here priests and doctors used a mixture of magical and practical methods of cure, just as people had done since prehistoric times.

SOURCE 5 – The god cured him

Aegestratos was unable to sleep because of headaches. As soon as he came to the temple he fell asleep and had a dream. He thought that the god cured him of his headache and, making him stand up, taught him wrestling. The next day he departed cured, and after a short time he competed at the Nemean games, and was victor in the wrestling.

Carved stone tablet found at a temple of Asklepios. Many similar tablets have been found.

❖ *How can cures like that of Aegestratos be explained?*
❖ *What effect would inscriptions like these have on sick people coming to be treated?*

SOURCE 6

Greek carving, 5th century BC. It shows the god Asklepios healing a patient.

MEDICINE IN ANCIENT ROME

Greek doctors in Rome – Galen

The greatest of the later Greek doctors was Galen. He was born at Pergamum, now in Turkey, about AD 130, and trained first at the temple of Asklepios in his home town and then at Alexandria. Later he worked for over 20 years in Rome – where most of the doctors were Greeks. He treated the Emperor Marcus Aurelius successfully and became Rome's leading doctor.

Galen gave lectures on medicine in Rome and wrote a series of books. He discussed the discoveries that had been made in the 500 years since Hippocrates, and he fitted them together into a single system. His books were to be used as textbooks for another 1400 years after his death, so he was of great importance in the history of medicine.

Galen's ideas

Galen strongly supported the theory of the four humours and based many treatments on it. But his main importance was in anatomy and in his ideas about the working of the body. At Alexandria he had been able to dissect human bodies, and he strongly recommended this to his students. It was still forbidden for religious reasons in other places. (See Source 1.) He described many features of the body far more exactly than the Indian books had done. Galen's observation was on the whole very accurate, and has impressed anatomists ever since.

Galen's main aim was to explain the purpose of each part of the body – what the heart, the arteries and the lungs do, and how they all work together. For example he showed that the brain controlled the body through the nerves. He did this by cutting through various nerves of a live pig and showing how this affected its ability to grunt or move. (See Source 2.)

Galen fitted his explanations in with the accepted theories like the theories of the four humours and the four elements. By his time the Greek thinkers, mainly at Alexandria, had put together a set of natural explanations for many things from the movement of the stars and the planets to the working of parts of the body. What Galen did was to give a complete account of the medical knowledge of his time and to show how it fitted in with the rest of Greek scientific thinking. As long as the Greek ideas were accepted as true it would be very difficult to disagree with Galen.

SOURCE 1 – How to study anatomy

Human bones are the subject which you should first get to know. At Alexandria this is very easy, since the physicians in that country let their students inspect human bodies for themselves. Try to get to Alexandria. But if you can't manage this it is not impossible to get to see human bones. I have often had a chance to do this where tombs have been broken. Once I examined the skeleton of a robber lying on a mountain-side. If you don't have the luck to see anything like this, you can still dissect an ape. For this you should choose apes which most resemble men. In the apes which walk and run on two legs you will also find the other parts as in man.

Galen, *On Anatomy*, Rome, c. AD 190

SOURCE 2

Galen dissecting a pig. From an edition of Galen's *Collected Works* published in Venice in 1556.

❖ *Sources 1 and 2 show that Galen dissected animals to learn about anatomy. Does this mean that his conclusions about human anatomy were likely to be reliable?*

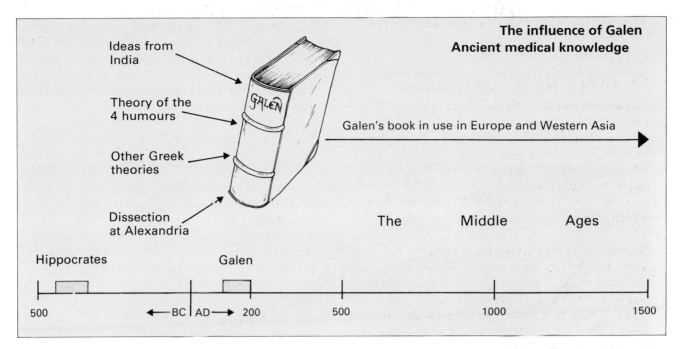

**The influence of Galen
Ancient medical knowledge**

Ideas from India

Theory of the 4 humours

Other Greek theories

Galen's book in use in Europe and Western Asia

Dissection at Alexandria

The   Middle   Ages

Hippocrates   Galen

500   ←BC | AD→ 200   500   1000   1500

The Romans – a public health system

Rome was much larger than any of the Greek cities. At the time of the birth of Christ it had a population of about a million. As it grew it faced major problems of water-supply and sewage. These problems were not new. Earlier cities, like Mohenjo Daro in India had built aqueducts to supply water and sewers to carry away waste. But the Roman system was on a much larger scale. About AD 100 there were nine aqueducts to bring water to Rome. There were filter tanks to purify it and lead pipes to take it to the houses of the rich and to the public baths. About 1000 million litres a day was supplied. In smaller towns and in army forts throughout the Empire there were similar systems.

How the water was used in Rome.

SOURCE 3 – Rome is healthier now

My job concerns not merely the convenience but also the health of the city.

The results of the great number of reservoirs, works, fountains and water basins can be seen in the improved health of Rome. The city looks cleaner, and the causes of the unhealthy air which gave Rome a bad name amongst the people in the past are now removed.

Compare such important engineering works with the idle pyramids and the useless though famous buildings of the Greeks!

Frontinus, *The Aqueducts of Rome*, c. AD 100. Frontinus was the official in charge of aqueducts.

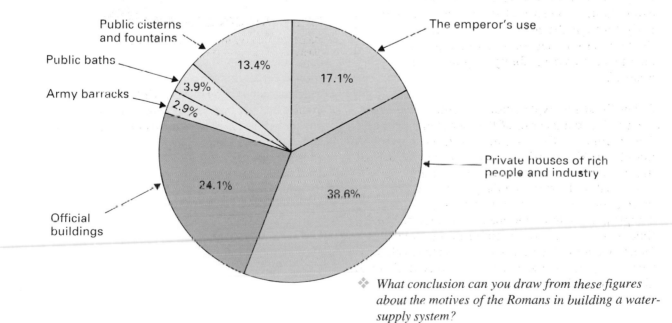

Public cisterns and fountains

Public baths

Army barracks

Official buildings

The emperor's use

Private houses of rich people and industry

13.4%
3.9%
2.9%
17.1%
24.1%
38.6%

❖ *What conclusion can you draw from these figures about the motives of the Romans in building a water-supply system?*

The Roman sewers

KEY QUESTION

◆ *Sources 1 to 6 suggest that the Romans tried to stay healthy. What do these sources tell us about Roman ideas on the causes of disease?*

The Romans built public and private lavatories. These are found all over the Empire, with well-designed drainage systems to carry away the sewage. In Rome there was a vast network of sewers. They deposited their foul contents into the river Tiber, which carried it down to the sea.

SOURCE 1

The outlet of the main Roman sewer into the river Tiber. From a drawing c. AD 1500.

SOURCE 2 – The sewers, the greatest achievement of all

Old men still admire the city sewers, the greatest achievement of all. They were built 700 years ago in the days of Tarquinius and they are still undamaged. Tarquinius is said to have made sewers large enough for a wagon load of hay to pass through. When Marcus Agrippa became Aedile (official in charge of the sewers) (33 BC) he travelled on a tour of inspection under the city in a boat. There are seven rivers made to flow in seven tunnels under the city. These finally run into one great sewer. They rush through like mountain streams and swollen with the rain water they sweep away all the sewage.

Pliny, *Natural History*, Rome, c. AD 50

SOURCE 3 – Keeping the army healthy

I will now give you some ideas about how the army can be kept healthy. Soldiers must not remain long near unhealthy marshes. A soldier who must face the cold without proper clothing is not in a state to have good health or to march. He must not drink swamp water. Daily exercise is better than the doctor for the soldiers. If a group of soldiers is allowed to stay too long in one place in the summer or autumn, they begin to suffer from the effects of polluted water, and are made miserable by the smell of their excrement. The air becomes unhealthy and they catch diseases. This has to be put right by marching to another camp.

Vegetius, Roman writer, 4th century AD

Artist's reconstruction of the bath at Aquae Sulis (Bath), Britain, built by the Romans in the 1st century AD.

SOURCE 5 – Watch out for bedpans

Along your route each open window may be a death-trap. So hope and pray, you poor man, that the local housewife drops nothing worse on your head than a bedpan full of slops.

Juvenal, *Satires*, Rome c. AD 100

SOURCE 6

The medicine of the ordinary people in ancient times

The medical ideas of doctors like Galen probably had little effect on the ordinary people. Only a few of the richer Romans could afford a doctor. The same was true in all the other early civilisations. Most people were still peasant farmers and lived in country villages where there were no doctors. Medical care was still mainly a matter for the family as it always had been.

SOURCE 7 – We need medicine, not doctors

a. Medicine changes day by day and we are swept away by the clever ideas of the Greeks. As if thousands of people could not live without physicians, though not, of course, without medicine! It was not medicine that our forefathers condemned, but the medical profession. They refused to pay fees to profiteers in order to save their lives. Of all the Greek arts it is only medicine which we Romans have not practised.

b. White of egg can help to heal wounds. Yolk of egg boiled hard in vinegar and roasted with pepper stops diarrhoea. Nits can be removed with dog fat.

Pliny, *Natural History*, Rome c. AD 50

❖ *What evidence can this source provide about the attitudes to medicine of:*
   a.   educated Romans like Pliny
   b.   poor people in the Roman world or those with little education?
❖ *What effect would the improved sewers and water supply have on the ordinary people who lived in Roman towns?*

Aqueduct at Nimes, France, built by the Romans in the 1st century AD.

MEDICINE IN THE MIDDLE AGES

1. Islamic medicine

KEY QUESTIONS

◆ *Islamic doctors produced many improvements but few ideas. How can this be explained?*

◆ *If this is true, why is Islamic medicine important in the history of medicine?*

About the year AD 500 the Roman Empire collapsed. In Western Europe there followed a period of great disorder. Cities were deserted and fell into ruin. Organised education and the training of doctors came to an end.

While this was happening in countries like Britain, a magnificent new civilisation was growing up in the Middle East. It was based on the new religion of Islam, which Muhammad founded in Arabia in 622. Islam swept rapidly through western and southern Asia, north Africa and parts of Europe. By AD 1000 Arabic was the main language of religion and learning from Spain to India. The capital of this Islamic Empire for a long time was Baghdad.

These pages tell you about the nature and importance of Islamic medicine.

Islam encouraged its believers to care for the sick, to build hospitals and to study medicine. The doctors at Baghdad were in an excellent position to gather together the ideas and books of Indian and Greek doctors.

The Islamic writers were full of admiration for the Greeks. They translated Hippocrates and Galen into Arabic, and followed their ideas closely. Islam taught that there was only one God, who made and controlled the world. Galen's idea that each part of the body had its own purpose fitted in well with this. It meant that the doctors following Galen's ideas were explaining the purposes of God.

For Islam the most important part of true knowledge was already written in the holy book, the Koran, and in the works of the Greeks. Dissection of the human body was forbidden by Islamic law. So they could not make major criticisms of the ideas of Galen.

One exception was a theory that was put forward by Ibn an-Nafis in Cairo in 1242. He disagreed with what Galen had said about the movement of blood in the heart. Ibn an-Nafis' view that it moved through the lungs is now accepted as correct. He based his ideas on his own observation, but no-one else took them up and the old view continued to be taught for another 300 years.

SOURCE 1

Arab drawing c. AD 1200, of Dioscorides teaching a student how to use a mandrake, a root used as a pain-killer. Dioscorides was a Greek who wrote a widely used book on drugs c. AD 60.

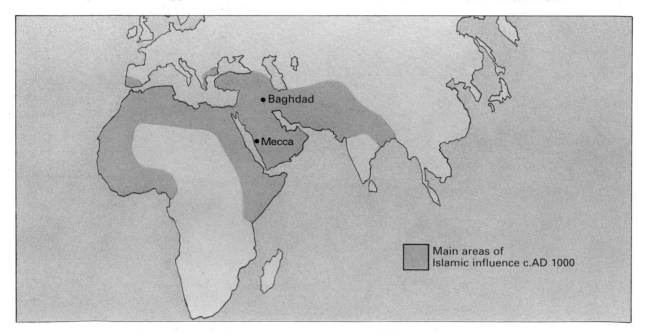

• Baghdad

• Mecca

Main areas of Islamic influence c.AD 1000

An 8th-century drawing of a baby being born by 'Caesarean section'. This operation was a last resort to save a living child from a dead or dying mother. It had been known to early Indian doctors and to the Greeks and Romans.

Although Islamic doctors mainly followed Greek ideas they did add many new items to medical knowledge. For instance the Persian doctor Rhazes (c.860–923) clearly described the differences between smallpox and measles for the first time.

SOURCE 3 – Rhazes describes smallpox

Smallpox is preceded by a continued fever, pain in the back, itching in the nose and terrors in the sleep. The symptoms of its approach are a pain in the throat and chest, a slight difficulty in breathing and a cough, a dryness of the mouth, thick spittle, hoarseness, headache, nausea and anxiety.

Rhazes, *Treatise on Smallpox and Measles*, Baghdad c.. 900 AD

One important Islamic contribution was in improving drugs and medicines. The Islamic 'alchemists' were searching for a way to turn other materials into gold. This seemed quite possible according to the Greek theories. Nobody ever succeeded in doing it, but in trying the alchemists developed new chemical apparatus. They were thus able to purify chemicals, and some of these, for instance alcohol, had a powerful effect on the human body.

Probably the most famous of the Islamic doctors was Ibn Sina, known later in Europe as Avicenna, who died in AD 1037. The textbook he wrote, called the *Canon of Medicine*, covered all aspects of the subject and was used for 600 years in Europe as well as throughout the Islamic world.

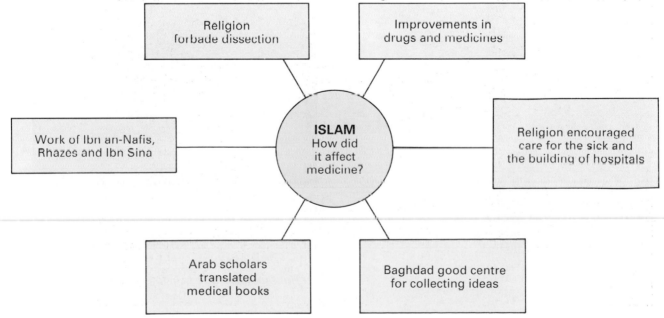

2. Christianity and medicine

KEY QUESTIONS

◆ *How did Christianity affect the development of medical knowledge?*

◆ *How did Christianity affect the development of treatment and cures?*

About the year AD 500 the Roman Empire in western Europe collapsed and a period of great disorder began. The only strong organisation to survive was the Christian Church. Its clergy could read Latin, and kept alive some memory of the medical ideas of writers like Galen.

The Christian Church taught that it was part of people's religious duty to care for the sick. But until about 1200 it did little to help in the study of medicine. St Bernard, founder of the Cistercian monasteries in the 12th century, said, 'To buy drugs or to consult with physicians doesn't fit with religion.' Faith, prayer, and the help of the saints seemed much more likely to be effective. So there was hardly any organised study of medicine or training of doctors in Christian Europe until about 1200.

This lack of doctors was probably not very important for most ordinary people. They continued to rely on traditional charms and herbs, and on care within the family or the village as they always had done.

After the year AD 1000 a period of prosperity began in Europe. Trade revived, farming improved, men began to build fine cathedrals, scholars could travel, study and write books more easily. After about AD 1200 universities were founded and the regular training of doctors began again.

These universities were controlled by the Church. They taught that the truth was mainly to be found by understanding books like the Bible or other writings from the past, like the books of Galen. The task of scholars was to make old ideas clear and not to start new ones.

The best places to study were at the Islamic universities in Spain, and the best books available were the Arabic books of the Islamic doctors. These, including the Arabic translations of Galen and Hippocrates, were now re-translated into Latin.

As they came to understand the ideas of the Greeks, European thinkers found that they fitted in very well with Christian ideas. The Greeks had said that the world of nature obeyed a set of laws. Now the Christians added that God, who made the world in the first place, also made the laws by which it worked. Christian doctors saw in Galen's books an explanation of how the parts of the body fitted in with God's purposes. So Galen's books, in a Latin translation of the Arabic translation of the Greek original, were nearly as much respected as the Bible.

SOURCE 1

Carving of Christ curing the leper c. 1000, Constantinople. The story is told in the New Testament.

SOURCE 2

King Edward the Confessor (d. 1066) touching a patient suffering from scrofula (an infection of the glands). Kings and queens of England until Queen Anne (d. 1714) claimed the power to cure this disease. Scrofula was known as 'The King's Evil'. Illustration from an English manuscript of the 13th century.

❖ *How does Source 1 help to explain this source?*

SOURCE 3 – Christian duty to the sick

Care for the sick stands before all. You must help them, as would Christ, whom you really help in helping them. Also you must bear patiently with them as in this way you gain greater merit. Let it also be a chief concern of the Abbot that the sick shall not be neglected at any single point.

Rules laid down by St Benedict for his monasteries, Italy c. AD 534.

SOURCE 4 – 'She gathered together all the sick'

Fabiola gathered together all the sick from the highways and the streets. She herself nursed the emaciated victims of hunger and disease. How often have I seen her wash wounds whose offensive stink stopped anyone else from even looking at them! She fed the sick with her own hands and revived the dying with nourishment.

Letters of St Jerome, c. AD 400, Italy. Fabiola was a wealthy Roman Christian. She died in AD 399.

SOURCE 5

Evil spirits being driven out before an altar; they can be seen coming out of the patient's mouth. Italian drawing, 17th century.

SOURCE 6

The Italian doctor, Mondino de Luzzi, teaching anatomy. From the 1493 edition of his book, first written in 1316. Galen had suggested that doctors should learn by dissecting the human body. The Christian Church did not completely forbid this, and in medical schools from about AD 1300 some dissections were carried out. This was to help the students to understand Galen's book, and not to encourage them to look and think for themselves. Mondino actually did the dissecting himself, but by the time this edition of his book was published this work was left to an assistant. What book is the teacher in the drawing likely to be using? Is he in a position to notice anything in the body that does not fit in with the book?

❖ *In what ways were medical ideas and methods the same in the Islamic as in the Christian regions in the years 500–1500?*
❖ *In what ways did they differ?*

CHANGES AND DEVELOPMENTS 500 BC – AD 1500: SUMMARY

The drawings below show some of the main changes that took place in medicine between 500 BC and AD 1500.

KEY QUESTIONS
- *What changes took place?*
- *Which aspects of medicine stayed the same?*
- *Why had things changed or stayed the same?*
- *Had these changes taken place quickly or slowly?*

500 BC   **AD 1500**

1. Doctors and medical knowledge

2. Surgery and anatomy

3. Public health systems

4. The medicine of ordinary people

Most people in 1500, even in civilised areas like India or Europe, were country people living in villages where there was no doctor. Perhaps the herbs, prayers and charms they used had been influenced by the clever ideas of educated people, but they had probably learned most of them from parents or neighbours.

WESTERN EUROPEAN MEDICINE 1500–1900

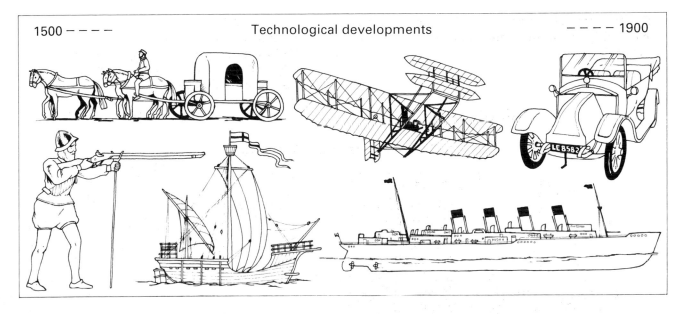

1500 – – – –   Technological developments   – – – – 1900

KEY QUESTION

◆ *How did changes in science and technology produce 'a new sort of medicine' by 1900 in Western Europe?*

Before 1500 Western Europe had not played a very important part in world history. Things were very different in the years 1500 to 1900. Europeans during this period invented new machines of many kinds – guns, better ships, steam engines and motor cars. Industrial towns developed and Europeans became rich and powerful. By 1900 they had used their power to conquer much of the rest of the world and to control its trade.

One reason for the great success of the Europeans was that they developed a new sort of science. This was based on the Greek method of careful observation and clear logical thinking, but European scientists went far beyond the work of the Greeks. European science was based on exact measurement and on experiments in a way that Greek science had never been. By 1900 they had used this to build up a very detailed explanation of the working of the natural world that was quite different from the explanations given by the Greeks or the Chinese.

These changes in technology and in science made for very great changes in medicine.

SOURCE 1

Leg amputation c.1550, from a contemporary drawing.

SOURCE 2

Early electrocardiograph for recording the electrical current in the feet. Photograph c.1911.

ANDREAS VESALIUS AND SCIENTIFIC ANATOMY

The Renaissance

KEY QUESTION
◆ *How did the Renaissance affect medical understanding?*

European scholars and artists of the 16th century were filled with admiration for the ancient Greeks. Artists tried to observe nature for themselves and to draw, carve and paint what they saw with their own eyes as the Greeks had done. Scholars searched for original copies of Greek books and translated them. Historians have called this renewed interest in ancient Greek attitudes the 'Renaissance' or re-birth. The new art of printing (invented about 1450) made it easy to spread these ideas throughout Europe.

SOURCE 1

SOURCE 2

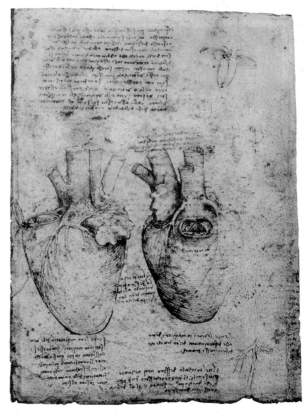

Leonardo da Vinci's drawing of a human heart, about 1512.

❖ *What evidence do Sources 1, 2 and 3 provide about changes in the attitude of artists during the Renaissance?*
❖ *How was this likely to affect medical understanding?*

SOURCE 3

Two lions – one drawn by Villard de Honnecourt, France c.1235 (left), and one by Albrecht Dürer, Germany, 1521 (right).

In 1531 Galen's books on anatomy were translated and published in Paris. Until then doctors had relied on copies translated centuries before, first into Arabic and then into Latin. Now that they could see the original they were very impressed with Galen's descriptions. His recommendation that they should look at the parts of the human body for themselves fitted in exactly with the Renaissance attitude.

Andreas Vesalius was a medical student at Paris when the new edition of Galen came out. He set out to follow Galen's advice. As a student he had some difficulty in getting bodies for dissection, but in 1537 he became Professor of Anatomy at the University of Padua in Italy. Here he had plenty of opportunity for dissection, and there were many artists with experience of drawing the human body in detail. The result was a book that is the foundation of modern scientific anatomy. *The Fabric of the Human Body*, published in 1543, was beautifully produced, using all the latest techniques of printing and of reproducing pictures. It gave a detailed description of all parts of the body, based directly on what Vesalius saw with his own eyes.

Vesalius had great respect for Galen, but as he did his dissection he discovered to his horror that Galen was sometimes wrong.

An important error in Galen's book was about the heart. Galen had said that the blood moved from one side of the heart to the other through holes in a thick membrane called the septum. Vesalius could see no such holes. At first this puzzled him.

Look at sources 4 and 5. Source 4 is from the first edition of Vesalius' book.

❖ *How did he explain the movement of the blood?*

Source 5 is from the second edition written twelve years later.

❖ *How has his explanation changed?*

It seems probable that he held the second opinion all the time.

❖ *Why then didn't he write it in the first edition?*

Vesalius' work did not mean that doctors stopped using Galen's book or believing his theories. But it did mean that they began to question them. If Galen and the Greeks could be wrong on one thing, they could be wrong on others. Vesalius was also important because he provided doctors for the first time with a clear and accurate picture of the structure of the body. This led them to ask how the parts of this structure worked together. If the blood could not move in the way Galen had said, how did it move?

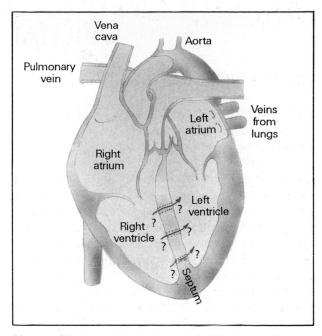

Diagram of the heart. Galen had argued that blood passes through holes in the septum. Vesalius could see no such holes.

SOURCE 4 – No holes to be seen

The septum of the heart is very dense. It has many pits on both sides, but none, so far as the senses can perceive, go right through from the right to the left ventricle. We are thus forced to wonder at the art of the Creator, by which the blood passes through from right to left through pores which cannot be seen.

Vesalius, *The Fabric of the Human Body*, first edition, 1543

SOURCE 5 – Galen must be wrong

Not long ago I would not have dared to diverge one hair's breadth from Galen's opinion. But the septum is as thick, dense and compact as the rest of the heart. I do not see therefore how the smallest particle can be transferred from the right to the left ventricle through it.

Vesalius, *The Fabric of the Human Body*, second edition, 1555

THE CIRCULATION OF THE BLOOD – WILLIAM HARVEY

The old theory of Galen

Vesalius' discovery that there were no holes in the septum of the heart was very awkward for people who wanted, as Vesalius did, to go on believing in the old-established theory of how the body works. Galen had known that the blood moves about the body through the veins and arteries. His theory had been that blood was made in the liver, mixed in the brain and the lungs with a substance known as 'spirit', and then used up in the other parts of the body. To get into the arteries it went through holes in the septum. If there were no such holes, how could it get into the arteries at all?

New theories

Realdo Columbo, who followed Vesalius as Professor at Padua, suggested part of the answer in 1559. He described how the blood circulated from the heart, through the arteries to the lungs, through the lungs and so back through the veins to the heart. The holes in the septum were no longer needed. Columbo had discovered part of the circulation – the movement of the blood through the lungs. But there were still many problems.

Soon after this another discovery was made at Padua. Fabricius, the next Professor after Columbo, discovered a system of one-way valves in the veins. This fitted in well with Columbo's ideas of blood flowing round in the same direction all the time.

The man who provided the final answer that is still accepted today was William Harvey. He was a student at Padua in the years 1600–1602, and Fabricius was his teacher, so he certainly learned about the valves.

Harvey also learned at Padua that the way to solve problems was by dissection and careful and exact experiment. He became a successful London doctor, but worked on steadily at his own research. Gradually he came to understand the whole system of circulation and he set out his views in a book *On the Movement of the Heart and Blood in Animals*, published in 1628.

Harvey proved, by trying to pump liquids the wrong way past the valves in veins and the arteries, that they were all one-way systems. He examined the valves and muscles of the heart itself, and saw that it worked like a water pump.

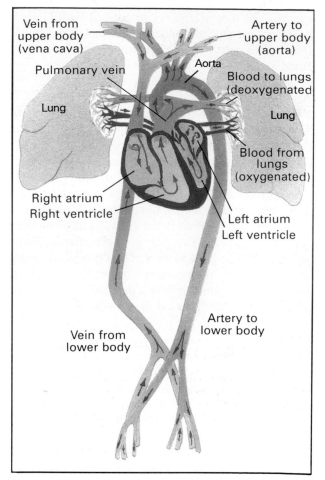

The circulation of the blood: As the walls of the left ventricle contract the blood is forced out into the great artery known as the aorta. From here it passes into smaller arteries and finally into the capillaries. In these vessels it begins its return journey to the heart through the veins, finally entering the right atrium of the heart through the vena cava. Then the blood passes through the right ventricle to the lungs where it is oxygenated before being returned to the left atrium. Then the blood passes into the left ventricle and begins to circulate through the body again.

SOURCE 1 – The heart works like a water pump

It is proved by the structure of the heart that the blood is transferred perpetually through the lungs into the aorta, as by two clacks (valves) of a water bellows to raise water.

Harvey's notes, 17 April 1616

He then went on to measure the amount of blood pumped by each heartbeat and to calculate the total amount pumped every hour. This was far more than could possibly be produced in the time by the food the person ate. So the same blood must keep on going round and round the whole body or circulating.

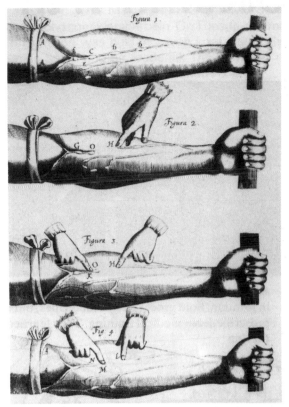

Diagram from Harvey's book. It shows an experiment to demonstrate the one-way valves in the veins. If the upper arm is bandaged as in Figure 1, the veins swell up. The valves then show up as lumps (G, O, H). If the finger is pressed along the vein from one valve to the next in the direction away from the heart (from O to H in Figures 2 and 3), the section of the vein between the valves is emptied of blood. It will *stay* empty. This is because valve O will not allow blood to flow away from the heart.

There was one serious difficulty. Harvey saw that the arteries as they got further and further from the heart divide into smaller and smaller branches until they are too small to see. In the same way the veins end in tiny hair-like blood vessels. For Harvey's theory to work the blood had to circulate through these tiny vessels from the arteries to the veins. This process cannot be seen by the human eye, but Harvey had enough confidence in his own work to insist that it must happen.

❖ *Why did other people believe Harvey?*
❖ *What arguments could he use to persuade those who didn't?*

Why Harvey's discovery was of very great importance . . .

1. Harvey's use of careful experiment and measurement impressed other scientific workers. He had used it to solve one important problem. Perhaps it could be used to solve others.
2. Harvey proved beyond any doubt that Galen and the Greeks had been wrong in their explanation of how one of the main parts of the body worked. Perhaps they were wrong on other things too.
3. Harvey's theory was widely accepted. Over the next 300 years doctors used it to build up knowledge of what the blood did in the various parts of the body as it circulated.

. . . but not until later

William Harvey's proof of the circulation of the blood was important for the development of science, and it was to lead to great improvement in medicine in the future. But in Harvey's lifetime it made no difference to the treatment given to patients, even by the doctors who fully understood it. In any case trained physicians like Harvey were very few in number. Most medical care was provided in other ways, as you can read on the next page.

35

YOUR CHOICE OF A DOCTOR IN 17TH-CENTURY ENGLAND

Background information

There were several possible ways of receiving medical treatment in 17th-century England. Here are some of them:

1. London physicians. All male, fully-qualified, university-trained. They charged very high fees.
2. London surgeons. Surgery was a separate job. Surgeons were inferior to physicians and were not allowed to prescribe medicine.
3. Country physicians. In the country the line between surgeons and physicians was much less clear. Dr Westover, for example, a Somerset physician, gave out medicines, pulled teeth, set broken limbs and did minor operations. Not as expensive as London physicians but still more expensive than most people could afford – they could charge 10 shillings (50p) for a visit, as much as a labourer might earn in two weeks.
4. Apothecaries. They had shops where they sold groceries and medicines. They had no medical training but learned on the job.
5. Market and fairground traders. No qualifications. Often did minor surgery and gave advice. Cheap.
6. Wise-women. In every village and town there were people, usually women, who gave medical advice and help to their neighbours. This was supplied free or very cheaply.

Which was the best?
What do the sources say?

Read the following sources and answer the questions which follow.

SOURCE 1

SOURCE 2

SOURCE 3

No one practises physic or professes midwifery, but charitably one neighbour helps another.

From the local records of Dry Drayton, Cambridgeshire, 1662

SOURCE 4

Everyone is a doctor. If you are ill, everyone you meet, whether a man or a woman, will prescribe a medicine for it.

Nicholas Culpeper, herbalist, 1649

SOURCE 5 – To cure malaria and the gout

Take the hair and nails of the patient, cut them small and either give them to the birds in a roasted egg, or put them in a hole in an oak tree. Stop up the hole with a peg of the same tree.

From *The New London Dispensary*, a book of remedies by W. Salmon, published in 1682.

SOURCE 6

His Majesty King Charles II had hurt his hand which he instructed his surgeons to make well. But they made it much worse so that it swelled and poisoned him up to the shoulder. He could not sleep and began to be feverish. Mrs Holder, wife of his chaplain, has a strange wisdom as to curing of wounds. Mrs Holder was sent for at 11 o'clock at night. She made ready a poultice and applied it and gave His Majesty sudden ease. Next day she dressed it and perfectly cured him, to the great grief of all the surgeons who envy and hate her.

From John Aubrey's *Brief Lives*, 1680.

SOURCE 7

The king laughs at medicine, declares physicians to be of very little use and hardly necessary. He says the art of medicine is supported by mere guesses and useless because uncertain.

Sir Thomas Mayerne, physician to King James I

SOURCE 8

I have swallowed the weight of an apothecary in medicine, and how much I am better for it I know not. I have learnt to bear my infirmities and not to trust to the skill of the physicians in curing them.

Elizabeth Montagu, early 18th century

SOURCE 9

2nd February   His Majesty was walking about when he felt some unusual disturbance in his brain, soon followed by loss of speech and convulsions. Two of the king's physicians opened a vein in his right arm and drew off about 16 ounces (450 ml) of blood. Within a few moments, to free his stomach from all impurities, they gave him an emetic (to make him vomit). Soon after they gave laxative pills so as to drain away all the humours. Over and above this, blistering agents were applied all over his head, after his hair had been shaved.

3rd February The physicians considered it necessary to open both jugular veins and draw off about 10 ounces (300 ml) of blood.

4th February The physicians considered it advisable to administer the following: spirit of human skull 40 drops.

6th February Every other hour, Oriental Bezoar stone, 2 scruples. (Bezoar is a green stone from the stomach of a Persian goat. A scruple is 1.3 grams.)

The king died soon after noon, towards the end of the 54th year of his age.

From an account of the death of Charles II written by Sir Charles Scarburgh, his Chief Physician.

QUESTIONS

1. Look at Sources 1 and 2. One of these two men is Sir Charles Scarburgh, Chief Physician to King Charles II. One is an ordinary physician-surgeon. Which is which? Give reasons for your decision.

2. Read Sources 3 and 4. Use the background information, the sources and your own knowledge to explain why most people consulted their neighbours and not a trained doctor when they wanted medical treatment.

3. It is difficult to find out about the kind of medical treatment most people received. How do you explain this?

4. Read Source 5. This remedy would be very unlikely to work. Why do you think it was collected and published?

5. Read Source 6. Why do you think the surgeons envied and hated Mrs Holder?

6. What do sources 1, 2, 3, 4, 5 and 6 tell us about the sorts of medical treatment available in 17th-century England?

7. Read sources 7 and 8. If people had these attitudes, why were there so many medical practitioners of different kinds in England?

8. Read Source 9. What theories about the causes of the king's illness do the physicians seem to have?

9. These were the best qualified doctors of their time. Why were they unable to do anything to help Charles II?

10. Do the sorts of medical practice described in these sources mean that the discoveries of Vesalius and Harvey were of no real importance?

11. 'Medicine in England in the 17th century was no better than it had been for hundreds of years before.' Is this statement true for:
   • everyone?
   • the rich?
   • the poor?
   • all diseases?

THE SCIENTIFIC REVOLUTION

KEY QUESTIONS
◆ *How did the scientific revolution affect medical knowledge?*
◆ *Did it produce any new cures?*

The work of Harvey did not lead to new methods of treating patients for over 200 years. But it did encourage the study of science. By 1700 the new science had been so successful that historians have described the change as the 'scientific revolution'. Its most impressive successes were in astronomy and physics. A series of European scientists used the new exact mathematical science to destroy the old Greek view of the universe completely. Isaac Newton measured the force of gravity exactly, and used this to explain in precise detail how the sun and planets moved. Newton showed clearly what his measurements were and how they fitted in with experiments made on Earth that anyone could check. Everybody who could understand his figures agreed that he was right. The navigators of 20th-century spaceships use Newton's systems.

Science and medicine

Newton's great success encouraged scientific work in other areas of knowledge. In some there were useful practical developments immediately – for instance the new scientific knowledge greatly improved navigation at sea. But in medicine scientific knowledge did not lead straight away to new cures. Building up scientific medicine was rather like climbing a mountain ridge. Once Vesalius had led the way up the first slope, Harvey could tackle the next. After Harvey's work others could climb higher still. Only when a series of doctors and scientists had climbed to the top of the ridge could they start to suggest useful treatments based on scientific knowledge. This did not happen until well after the year 1800. There were two reasons for the delay.

1. Microscopes were needed

Many important parts of the body, like the capillaries, are too small to see with the naked eye. The bacteria that cause many diseases are even smaller. The first microscopes were made in Harvey's lifetime. In 1661 Marcello Malpighi of Padua saw for the first time the fine blood vessels or 'capillaries' which Harvey had said must exist.

Other discoveries were made with these early microscopes, but their power was very limited. Until about 1830 they were not powerful enough for the detailed study of bacteria to begin.

2. Chemistry was needed

The chemicals that make up the human body are very complex. Before it could be understood simple chemicals had to be identified. Even the air we breathe turned out to be not an element, as the Greeks had thought, but a mixture of several gases. The most important of these for life, oxygen, was not identified until 1777. So chemists could not begin to explain what happened to it or to other chemicals inside the human body until well into the 19th century.

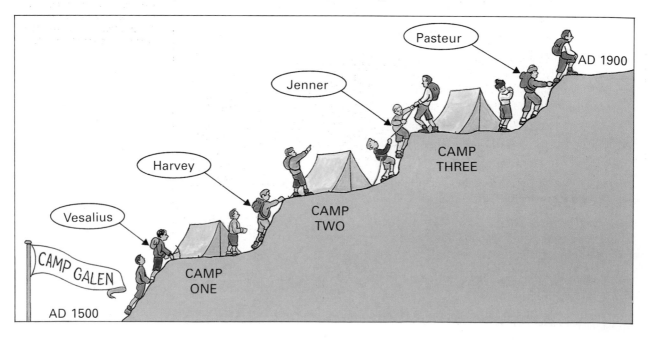

Better education for doctors

The new science did not help doctors of the 17th or 18th century to find new cures for any diseases. This does not mean that it was of no use to them. In the medical schools of the universities the training became much more scientific. Doctors had to understand anatomy in detail and study chemistry and botany. By the 18th century clinical observation in a hospital was also included as part of an up-to-date medical course. The result was that in the 18th century many European doctors were better trained and observed their patients more carefully. Some of them applied their scientific training to what they saw. Edward Jenner was one doctor who did this.

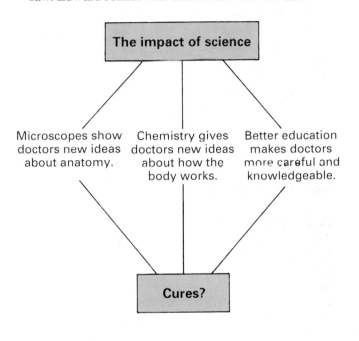

The impact of science

Microscopes show doctors new ideas about anatomy.

Chemistry gives doctors new ideas about how the body works.

Better education makes doctors more careful and knowledgeable.

Cures?

Jenner and smallpox vaccination

Smallpox was a disfiguring disease that was sometimes fatal. It was very common, but people knew that, as with many other diseases, someone who had once recovered from it did not usually catch it again. Cows suffer from a similar disease, cowpox, and country people in the 18th century knew that milkmaids who had caught cowpox did not catch smallpox afterwards.

Jenner was a scientifically trained doctor and a Fellow of the Royal Society. In 1796 he decided to test the stories about cowpox and carried out an experiment by infecting a boy, James Phipps, with it. Then he scratched the boy's arm and put material from a smallpox patient into the scratch. James did not develop smallpox. Jenner went on to develop a method of using the 'lymph', or cowpox material, from one patient to spread the disease to another. He did this to 23 patients one after the other and found that the last of them was still protected against smallpox. In 1798 he announced his new method, which he called 'vaccination', from the Latin word 'vacca', meaning a cow. Some doctors and others opposed him, but vaccination was widely adopted. It was made compulsory in parts of Germany in 1807 and in Britain in 1853. By 1980 vaccination had wiped out smallpox all over the world.

❖ *Why should people oppose so useful a discovery as vaccination?*
❖ *Jenner had no idea how vaccination worked inside the body. Does this mean that his discovery was not a scientific one?*

SOURCE 1

'The cowpock – or the wonderful effects of the new inoculation', a cartoon by James Gilray, published by the Anti-Vaccine Society in 1802.

MEN TAKE OVER MORE OF MEDICINE

KEY QUESTIONS
◆ *Why were men opposed to women being involved in medicine?*
◆ *Why were women able to continue to do medical work despite this opposition?*

Ever since the early civilisations nearly all doctors have been men. This is partly because at most times and places women have not normally been taught to read or allowed to train as doctors. But trained doctors were few in number, and most medical care was carried out by other people – often women. For instance until about AD 1600 all midwives were women. Many women were skilled with herbs, bandages and poultices, and were consulted by friends or neighbours. Sometimes they were paid.

We have seen that in the 17th and 18th centuries the education and training of doctors improved a great deal. It was based now on the new anatomy of Vesalius and on the new science. But women were excluded from the universities and from most education, as they had been since ancient times. So as medicine became more scientific women played a less and less skilled part in it. The improvements in the education and training of doctors helped to drive women out of the more respectable and better paid sorts of medical work.

The sources on this page provide evidence about the role of women in medicine.

SOURCE 1 – In case of difficulty a doctor should be called

For a normal birth the delivery should be carried out by four women, stout hearted and of riper years, who shall trim their nails well. In difficult cases a doctor should be called. If the child's body is wrongly placed, it should be manipulated until the head is brought down. If this fails the doctor must resort to the knife.

Susruta Samhita, India, before AD 200

SOURCE 2 – Women doctors attacked

Worthless and presumptuous women usurp this profession. Possessing neither natural ability nor professional knowledge, they make the greatest possible mistakes thanks to their stupidity, and very often kill the patients. For they work without wisdom and from no certain foundation of knowledge, but in a casual fashion.

John of Mirfield, a physician at St Bartholomew's Hospital, London, 14th century.

SOURCE 3

16th-century woodcut of midwives delivering a baby from J. Rueff, *De Conceptu*, Frankfurt, 1580.

❖ *What are the men in the background doing?*
❖ *What opinions might the men and the women have of the importance of their two different roles?*

SOURCE 4 – Women not to meddle with surgery

There are divers women and others within the City altogether unskilled in the art of surgery who do oftentimes take great cures upon them to the great danger of the patient. It is therefore ordered that no such woman meddle with any surgery for which they shall have taken any money benefit or reward.

Regulations by Salisbury City Council, 1614

SOURCE 5 – Paying a woman surgeon

My maid being sick I paid for opening her vein 4 pence (1.5p) to the Widow Rugglesford. For looking to her I gave 1 shilling (5p), and to old Bess for tending her 3 days and 2 nights I gave 1 shilling. In all two shillings and 4 pence (11.5p).

The Revd Giles Moore's Diary, 1667. At this time one shilling (5p) was about a day's wage for a labourer.

SOURCE 6 – Women's advice trusted

Mr Hobbes used to say that he had rather have the advice or take medicine from an experienced old woman, that had been at many sick people's bedsides, than from the learnedest but unexperienced physician.

John Aubrey, *Brief Lives* c.1680. Thomas Hobbes was a famous philosopher.

The male midwife

Doctors had always claimed the right to supervise the work of midwives. About 1620 Peter Chamberlen, an English surgeon, invented the obstetric forceps for use in difficult deliveries. They made it possible to free a baby without killing it. For a time the design was kept secret by the Chamberlen family. To use the forceps anatomical knowledge was needed, and they were used only by men. By 1700 fashionable ladies in English thought it safer to employ a man as midwife than to rely on the help of local women.

SOURCE 7

18th-century Dutch engraving of male midwife from S. Janson, *Korte en bondige verhandeling*, 1711.

SOURCE 8

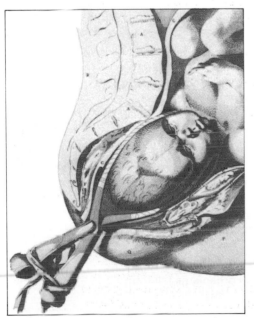

Forceps as used by doctors in the 18th century from W. Smellie, *Tabulae Anatomicae*, Frankfurt, 1786.

Many people still rely on unqualified medical care

The changes that squeezed women out of medical work had far less effect among the poorer classes than among the rich. In the 19th century midwifery and much other medical care for most people was still provided by experienced but unqualified friends and neighbours.

SOURCE 9

Woman collecting herbs, from a 1476 version of Pliny's *Natural History*.

SOURCE 10 – Nurse, washerwoman and herbalist 1834

Alice had been out all day in the fields, gathering wild herbs for drinks and medicines, for in addition to her valuable qualities as a sick nurse and her worldly occupation as a washerwoman, she added a considerable knowledge of hedge and field simples; and on fine days she used to wander off into the lanes and meadows.

Her room was oddly festooned with all manner of hedgerow, ditch and field plants, which we are accustomed to call valueless, but which have a powerful effect either for good or for evil and are consequently much used among the poor. The room was strewed, hung and darkened with these bundles, which emitted no very fragrant odour in the process of drying.

Description of a Manchester herb seller, from Elizabeth Gaskell's novel *Mary Barton*, 1834. Elizabeth Gaskell was the wife of a Manchester clergyman and knew the houses of the poor well.

HOW WERE GERMS DISCOVERED?
LOUIS PASTEUR AND ROBERT KOCH

An old theory

People had known for thousands of years that some diseases are infectious – they spread easily from one person to another. In Greek and Roman times people thought this was due to 'bad air' influenced perhaps by the stars. By 1800 people who understood science no longer believed in the influence of the stars on health, but bad air seemed as reasonable a cause as ever.

What causes decay?

Since ancient times people had believed that the worms and maggots found in decaying meat somehow grew out of the meat. As microscopes improved, new evidence seemed to confirm this. Scientists could see that living and decaying matter was full of microscopic living creatures, which they called microbes or germs. Where did they come from? It seemed reasonable to suggest that the microbes grew out of decaying animal or vegetable matter like the maggots. Scientists called the process 'spontaneous generation'.

A new theory

Some scientists of the early 19th century made a different suggestion. Perhaps microbes were the cause of the decay and not the result. Perhaps they could float about in the air, and thus spread decay. If this was so some of them might also spread disease. This theory meant that the ordinary air which everyone breathed all the time was full of tiny living creatures that could cause decay and disease. It was very difficult to persuade people that anything as unlikely as that could be true.

Pasteur proves that germs cause decay

Louis Pasteur was Professor of Chemistry at Lille in France, when a local brewer asked for his help. The fermentation process to make alcohol was going wrong. Pasteur found harmful micro-organisms in large numbers in the vats, and set to work to find how they got there.

In a series of careful experiments he proved that the microbes that cause things to go bad float about in the air.

SOURCE 1

Pasteur at work in his laboratory.

❖ *What new technologies is Pasteur using?*

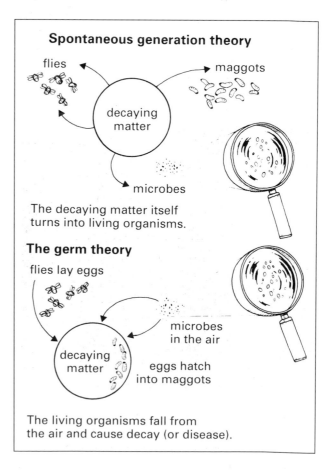

Spontaneous generation theory

flies

maggots

decaying matter

microbes

The decaying matter itself turns into living organisms.

The germ theory

flies lay eggs

decaying matter

microbes in the air

eggs hatch into maggots

The living organisms fall from the air and cause decay (or disease).

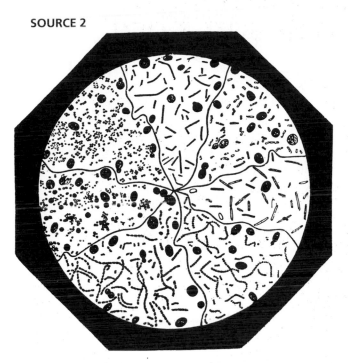

Drawing of different types of micro-organisms found in beer. Louis Pasteur, *Studies on Beer*, Paris, 1876. The large dark blobs are yeast organisms and the smaller, fainter ones are various types of harmful microbes.

SOURCE 3

Cartoon showing Koch as St George slaying the dragon c.1880.

❖ *The cartoon on page 39 shows that some people opposed Jenner. This cartoon shows Koch as a hero, and he met little public opposition. How can this contrast be explained?*

In 1861 Pasteur published his results. After that any scientist could repeat Pasteur's experiment to check it, so nobody could argue for long that germs were not the cause of decay. Pasteur went on to show that some diseases of plants and animals were caused by germs, but he was not a doctor and did not himself prove that they cause diseases in humans. In 1865, when an epidemic of cholera hit France, Pasteur tried hard to identify the germ that carried the disease, but he failed. It was Robert Koch who took this final step to establish the germ theory of disease.

Koch proves that germs cause diseases in humans

Robert Koch was a German doctor and also a very careful and determined scientific researcher. He had read of Pasteur's discoveries and he began in 1872 to look for the microbes in diseased animals and people. He found a way to stain them so that he could see them clearly and photograph them through his microscope. In this way he could identify them without any argument. He then carried out careful tests to prove beyond doubt that the microbe that he suspected did in fact cause the disease he was studying.

In 1878, Koch himself discovered the microbes that cause wounds to go septic and later those that cause several diseases. In 1880 he was given an official post in a German government laboratory, and by 1900 he and his students had identified the germs causing 21 diseases. The search for microbes had become the new science of bacteriology.

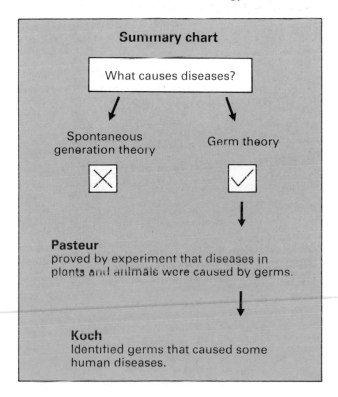

Summary chart

What causes diseases?

Spontaneous generation theory ✗

Germ theory ✓

Pasteur
proved by experiment that diseases in plants and animals were caused by germs.

Koch
Identified germs that caused some human diseases.

Results of the germ theory

The germ theory was a breakthrough of great importance. Modern science had at last arrived at the top of part of the mountain that men like Vesalius and Harvey had begun to climb 300 years earlier – precise and certain causes for some diseases had been found. This meant that doctors trying to prevent and cure them would have some real chance of success. Most of these successes took place in the 20th century, but two important ones were made in the 1880s and 1890s.

1. More vaccinations to prevent diseases

Pasteur was very interested in the system of smallpox vaccination that Jenner had developed. It seemed likely that when someone was vaccinated, disease germs were put into their bloodstream. The disease germs of cowpox must somehow protect the body against those of smallpox. In 1880, Pasteur and his assistants were studying how the disease of chicken cholera could be spread from one bird to another when by accident they used material containing germs that were several days old. They found that it worked like vaccination and protected the chickens against the disease. So they called the material they used a 'vaccine'.

In 1881 Pasteur and his team used similar methods to produce a vaccine against anthrax (a severe bacterial infection of cattle and humans), and in 1884 another against rabies, a disease spread by the bite of an infected dog.

SOURCE 1

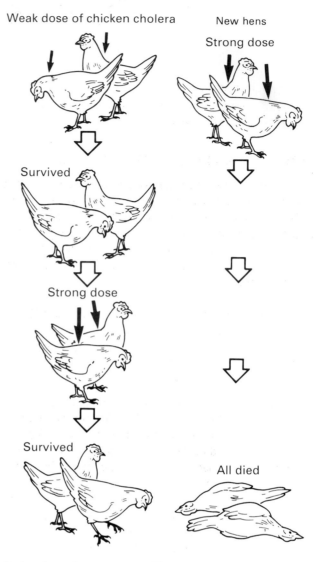

Weak dose of chicken cholera — New hens, Strong dose — Survived — Strong dose — Survived — All died

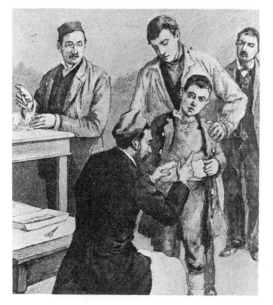

Joseph Meister aged 9, the first human to be vaccinated against rabies, 1885. He had been bitten by a mad (rabies-infected) dog. Vaccination saved him from almost certain death.

2. Anti-toxins to cure diseases

Vaccination is a method of preventing disease. It was Koch's assist ant Emil Behring who produced the first actual cure based on the germ theory. Pasteur's team had discovered that germs cause disease by producing poisons, or 'toxins', in the blood-stream. Behring then found that some animals produced an 'anti-toxin' in their blood to fight the poison.

This substance could be extracted and injected into humans where it in turn would destroy the poisons caused by the germs. On Christmas Day 1891, a child was cured of diphtheria (a bacterial infection which blocks the throat) by the first use of the anti-toxin.

After 1900 many other vaccines and anti-toxins were developed using the methods pioneered by Pasteur, Koch and Behring.

CHANGES IN SURGERY

KEY QUESTIONS
◆ *How were surgical operations made painless?*
◆ *How were they made safer?*

Operations before anaesthetics

Until the 19th century any operation, even pulling a tooth out, could cause almost unbearable pain. Patients had sometimes to be held down and the surgeon had to do his work as quickly as possible. Drugs like alcohol and opium might help to dull the pain, but surgeons had to be tough and quick and patients brave.

SOURCE 1 – Like a criminal preparing for execution

Several years ago I was required to prepare for the loss of a limb by amputation. Suffering so great as I underwent cannot be expressed in words.

Before the days of anaesthetics a patient preparing for an operation was like a condemned criminal preparing for execution. He counted the days till the appointed day came. He counted the hours of that day. He listened for the surgeon's carriage, his pull on the door bell, his foot on the stair. He watched for the production of his dreaded instruments, for his few grave words. I still recall the spreading out of the instruments, the first incision, and the bloody limb lying on the floor. From all this I should have been saved by ether or chloroform.

When I first heard that anaesthetics had been discovered I could not believe it. I have since thanked God that he has put it into your heart to devise so simple and safe a way of lessening pain.

From a letter to Sir James Simpson, discoverer of chloroform anaesthesia.

❖ *What skills were needed by surgeons like those in Sources 1 and 2?*
❖ *Why were operations done in people's homes, not in hospitals?*

SOURCE 2

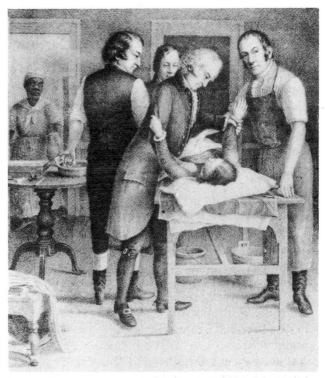

An operation to remove a woman's ovaries being carried out in 1809. The patient was strapped to the kitchen table and sang hymns to counteract the pain. Contemporary illustration.

SOURCE 3 – Robert Liston: high-speed surgeon

Liston's second most famous case
He amputated a leg in 2½ minutes, but in his enthusiasm the patient's testicles as well.

Liston's most famous case
He amputated a leg in under 2½ minutes. The patient died afterwards in the ward from hospital gangrene – they usually did in those pre-Listerian days. He amputated in addition the fingers of his young assistant, who also died afterwards in the ward from hospital gangrene. He also slashed through the coat tails of a distinguished surgical spectator, who was so terrified that the knife had pierced his vitals that he dropped dead from fright.

That was the only operation with a 300 per cent mortality.

R. Gordon, *Great Medical Disasters*, 1983. Robert Liston was the first man in Europe to perform an operation under anaesthetic – in under 2½ minutes.

The first anaesthetics

In the late 18th century the new science of chemistry was making great progress. Among the newly discovered chemicals was a gas, nitrous oxide or 'laughing gas'. Humphrey Davy, the young scientist who discovered it, noticed that it dulled the feeling of pain. In 1799 he wrote 'It seems capable of destroying pain and might probably be used in surgical operations.' The first person to try this was an American dentist, Horace Wells, in 1844. Meanwhile the chemists discovered other possible anaesthetics. Ether was the first of these to be used.

Ether was more reliable than laughing gas. But in 1847 James Y. Simpson, a leading Edinburgh surgeon, began to use chloroform. This worked better still and Simpson used it both in childbirth and in general operations.

Despite this some people opposed anaesthetics.

❖ *What differences would anaesthetics make to the skills doctors needed?*
❖ *Why did some doctors prefer to operate without anaesthetics?*

SOURCE 1

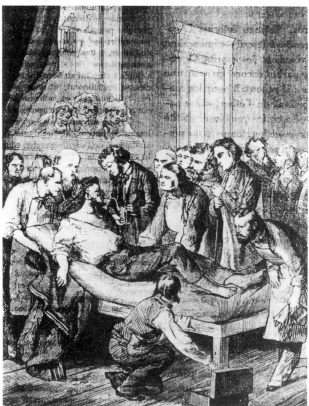

William Morton using ether in an operation in Boston, USA in 1846. As described in Source 2.

The introduction of anaesthetics

1799	Humphrey Davy noticed the value of 'laughing gas'.
1844	First use of 'laughing gas' by American dentist.
1847	Simpson began to use chloroform.
1853	Queen Victoria given chloroform for the birth of her eighth child.

SOURCE 2 – The patient suffered no pain

Dr Warren (the surgeon), announced that a test of some preparation was to be made for which the astonishing claim had been made that it would render the person operated upon free from pain.

Dr Morton entered. Dr Warren turned to him and in a strong voice said, 'Well, Sir, your patient is ready.' In a few minutes he was ready for the surgeon's knife, when Dr Morton said, 'YOUR patient is ready, sir.'

The operation was for a tumor on the left side of the neck. The operation was successful and when the patient recovered he declared that he had suffered no pain. Dr Warren turned to those present and said, 'Gentlemen, this is no humbug.'

Washington Ayer, an eye-witness of the operation, *The Semi-Centennial of Anaesthesia*, USA, 1897.

SOURCE 3 – All pain is destructive

Our successors in years to come will marvel at the idea of humane men confessing that they prefer operating on their patients in a waking instead of an anaesthetic state; and that the fearful agonies that they inflict should be endured quietly and not avoided.

All pain is destructive and even fatal in its actions and effects.

James Y. Simpson, speaking to the Medico-Chirurgical Society of Edinburgh, 1 December 1847.

SOURCE 4 – Birth-pains are natural and useful

a.   It is repulsive to good taste and sound judgement that every woman about to pass through the ordeal to which she was doomed by the laws of Nature should be henceforth rendered insensible through the whole of the proceedings.

b.   The infliction has been invented by Almighty God. Pain may even be considered a blessing of the Gospel, and being blessed admits of being met either well or ill.

c.   It is a most unnatural practice. The pain and sorrow of labour exert a most powerful and useful influence upon the religious and moral character of women and upon all their future relations in life.

Letters to the *Lancet*, a periodical for surgeons, 1848, 1849 and 1853. At this time all surgeons were men.)

SOURCE 5

Hannah Greener, aged 15, the first person to die under chloroform, 1848. Her operation was for the removal of a toenail.

SOURCE 6 – Dead in two minutes

The inhalation was done from a handkerchief on which a teaspoonful of chloroform had been poured. In about half a minute, finding her insensible, I requested Mr Lloyd to begin the operation. She gave a kick which caused me to think that the chloroform had not had sufficient effect. I was proceeding to apply more when her lips became suddenly blanched and she spluttered at the mouth. I threw down the handkerchief, dashed cold water in her face, and gave her some internally, followed by brandy, without, however, the least effect. The whole process of inhalation, operation and death could not have occupied more than two minutes.

London Medical Gazette, 1848, describing Hannah Greener's operation.

Anaesthetics accepted

It took Simpson and his friend several years to persuade most doctors and patients that anaesthetics were safe and effective (see source 3).

Simpson was one of Queen Victoria's doctors. In 1853 she asked to be given chloroform at the birth of her eighth child. After that it was very difficult for doctors to refuse it to others, and it came into widespread use in the next few years.

Although anaesthetics made operations less painful, it did not make them much safer. Surgeons could now try longer and more complicated operations (see source 7).

SOURCE 7 – 80 per cent died

Ovariotomy (removal of diseased ovaries) was coming along and one of our surgeons was keen on it. His mortality was around 80 per cent. I used to dread seeing the notice of the operation, as I knew that in a few days the patient would probably be lying on the post-mortem table.

An old sister who had spent her life in the service of the hospital once said sadly to me, 'I really do not think that the physicians do much good, and as for the surgeons, I think that they do as much harm as they do good.'

J. R. Leeson, *Lister as I knew him*, 1927, writing of his own experience in the 1860s.

SOURCE 8 – Stained with blood and spotted with pus

One of our surgeons lectured upon anatomy in an old frock-coat. I see him now, pawing the dissection as he lectured upon it. When it was past even this work he took it up to the operating theatre. The idea was a good one. Why should he soil a good frock-coat when a discarded one was available? An operation was a dirty job and an old coat was a suitable garment. I see it now, all faded with age, stained with blood and spotted with pus.

A rival to this coat was the 'ward sponge'. It appeared at all dressings. It was simply wrung out in warm water and passed from case to case.

J. R. Leeson, *Lister as I knew him*, 1927, writing of the 1870s.

❖ *Why did the use of anaesthetics make operations more dangerous?*

Lister and antiseptic surgery

In 1865 Joseph Lister was Professor of Surgery at Glasgow. He was worried about the number of his patients whose wounds turned septic after their operations. His friend the Professor of Chemistry told him of Pasteur's work and Lister saw immediately that microbes in the air or on dressings might carry the infection.

Lister knew that carbolic acid had been used to make sewage safe to use as fertiliser. Perhaps it worked by killing the microbes. If this was right the acid might also kill the microbes that made his patients' wounds turn septic. So Lister tried out carbolic acid as an 'antiseptic'. He used the acid in various ways, including spraying it in the air, in his attempt to kill all the microbes on or near the patient.

Carbolic acid was very unpleasant for doctors and nurses and sometimes harmed the patient. But the results were quite clear.

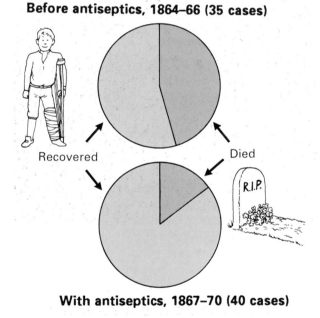

Before antiseptics, 1864–66 (35 cases)

Recovered   Died

With antiseptics, 1867–70 (40 cases)

SOURCE 1 – Everything was soaked in carbolic

Everything was soaked in a 1 in 20 solution of carbolic, hands, instruments and patients' skins. Moreover, the whole scene of the operation or dressing was enveloped in its spray. It went into every nook and cranny of the wound. Our faces and coat sleeves often dripped with it. Needless to say carbolic acid made sad work with our hands, which were always rough and cracked.

J. R. Leeson, *Lister as I knew him*, 1927.

SOURCE 2

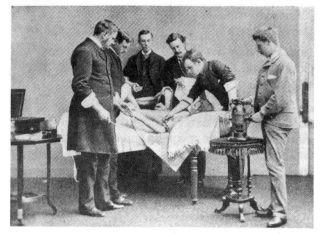

Photograph of an operation c.1880, Aberdeen. The carbolic spray is on the table on the right.

SOURCE 3 – Opposition to antiseptics

a.   The hospital was nursed by the St John's sisters who thought the be-all of their mission was for the patients to have shining faces, tidy lockers and to say their prayers often. They resented the extra work antiseptics gave them, the endless washing of basins and mackintoshes.

The hostility to antiseptics was extraordinary. One of the surgeons at St Bartholomew's Hospital could always raise a laugh by telling anyone who came into the operating room to shut the door quickly lest one of Mr Lister's microbes should come in.

J. R. Leeson, *Lister as I knew him*, 1927.

b.   Amongst other things it was very difficult to convince surgeons that tiny objects about 1/20000 of an inch (0.001 mm) in diameter could be the cause of the septic disease. The surgeons of that day were interested in keeping up their anatomy and in acquiring great rapidity in operating. Minute germs seemed far removed from practical work.

W. Watson Cheyne, one of Lister's assistants, *Joseph Lister*, 1927.

❖ *We find it easy to understand the importance of germs and antiseptics. Why did well-educated doctors find it difficult in the 1880s?*

Nurses help to make the new methods possible

The operation shown on page 48 is not being carried out in a hospital. Before the coming of antiseptics there was far more danger of infection in hospital than at home. So rich people paid for the surgeon to come to their homes and hospitals were mainly for the poor.

Another reason for this was that it was not until about this time that the properly organised training of nurses began. Starting in the 1850s, Florence Nightingale fought hard to make nursing into a respectable profession. Her success nursing the soldiers during the Crimean War (1854–6) made her a national heroine and this encouraged others. So as antiseptics and other new methods came into use, educated nurses who knew now to use them gradually became available. Without this the more complicated operations made possible by anaesthetics and antiseptics could not have happened.

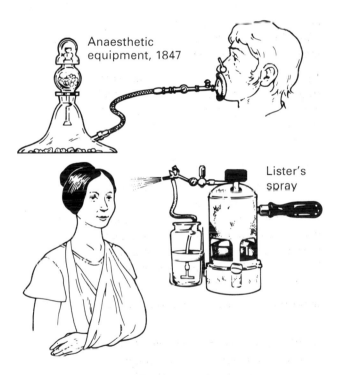

Anaesthetic equipment, 1847

Lister's spray

Florence Nightingale in 1855.

Anaesthetics and antiseptics

1847	Simpson's use of choroform.
1861	Pasteur's publications.
1865	Lister's experiments with carbolic acid.

The impact of antiseptics

Antiseptic surgery spread rapidly in the 1870s and 1880s. As with other new systems it was greatly improved later, but Lister's work was the real beginning of modern surgery. Until this time any serious operation had been a desperate and dangerous remedy that often failed. Now operations on the surface of the body could be done with safety, and surgeons could begin to work deep inside the body.

PUBLIC HEALTH IN 19TH-CENTURY BRITAIN

SOURCE 1

A London backstreet in the 1870s. Contemporary drawing by Gustav Doré.

KEY QUESTIONS

◆ *Why were 19th-century industrial towns in Britain so unhealthy?*

◆ *What was done to deal with public-health problems?*

The early cities in the ancient world, like Mohenjo Daro or Rome, had had to face health problems that did not exist in the villages of prehistoric times. In the 19th century Britain became the first industrialised nation and the first industrial cities had to face another set of health problems.

As more and more people crowded into the factory towns to work, houses were built as close together as possible. Many of them were damp and overcrowded. Most towns had no sewers, and everywhere there were stinking toilets and piles of filth. The filth soaked into rivers or wells and then drinking water was taken from them. People had to cook and eat food in dirty conditions. All these things encouraged disease, especially amongst the poor, who lived in the worse places.

In 1839 an official enquiry into the living conditions of the poor was set up, and in 1842 it produced a report. This made three main recommendations for industrial towns:

1. Drainage and refuse collection should be organised.
2. A pure water supply should be provided.
3. A Medical Officer of Health should be appointed.

SOURCE 2 – Average age of death in 1842

Type of people	Leeds (town areas)	Rutlandshire (country area)
Professional persons, gentry and their families	44	52
Farmers, tradesmen and their families	27	41
Mechanics, labourers and their families	19	38

Figures from Edwin Chadwick's *Report on the Sanitary Condition of the Labouring Population of Great Britain*, 1842.

For over 30 years an argument went on about the need for town councils or the Government to carry out suggestions like this. In the 1840s some towns, like Liverpool and Manchester, did start to build sewage and water-supply systems. A few appointed a doctor as Medical Officer of Health to supervise them. But many towns, like Leeds, refused to do this and Parliament would not pass laws to make it compulsory. A Public Health Act passed in 1848 was not effective. Finally, in 1875, Parliament passed a Public Health Act which said that all town councils had to build effective sewers and water systems and appoint a qualified doctor as medical officer.

Why did Parliament agree to this in 1875, when for over thirty years it had refused to do so? During that period three things happened that may have influenced the decision.

1. Health in many towns continued to be very bad. In 1865 there was an epidemic of cholera that killed 14 000 people in England and Wales.
2. In 1861 Pasteur had proved that germs cause decay. It seemed very likely that germs caused diseases too, though Koch did not prove this until 1878.
3. In 1867 the vote was given to all male householders in the towns. Until then only the richer classes had been able to vote.

❖ *How might each of these things have influenced Parliament?*

The Public Health Act of 1875 was very effective. By 1900 most British towns had built up effective and hygienic sewers and water systems.

SOURCE 3 – 75 tons of manure in one yard

In Boot and Shoe Yard in Leeds there are 34 houses and there dwell in these houses 340 people, or ten to every house. In the days of the cholera the Commissioners removed from it 75 cartloads of manure which had been untouched for years.

A house of this description will contain a cellar, a living room and a bed room. To build the largest number of cottages on the smallest space seems to have been the original view of the speculators. Thus neighbourhoods have arisen in which there is neither water nor offices (toilets).

Robert Baker, *An Inquiry into the Condition of the Town of Leeds*, 1842.

❖ *When conditions were as bad as this, why did towns like Leeds refuse to make the changes recommended in the 1842 report?*

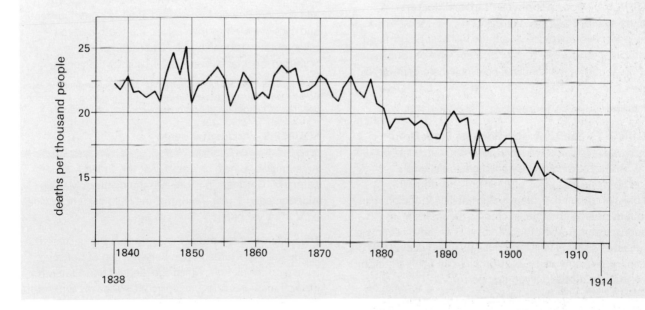

The graph above shows the death rate in England and Wales for the years 1838–1914.

❖ *Which changes shown in this graph might be partly the result of the improved public health system after 1875?*

❖ *Other medical developments took place during the period covered by this graph. Would any of them be likely to have affected the death rate?*

❖ *What non-medical changes might have affected the deathrate?*

HOW DID THE MEDICAL CHANGES HELP ORDINARY PEOPLE IN 19TH-CENTURY BRITAIN?

Background information

As medicine became more scientific, the education and training needed by a doctor became longer and more expensive. So doctors' fees increased and many people could not afford them. But, as in earlier periods of history, there were plenty of other sources of medicine and advice.

People in country villages could gather or grow herbs to make medicines, and were often skilled in their use. But people living in towns could not do this. So there was a ready market for shopkeepers selling medicines, many of them made from herbs. As newspapers and advertising became common the firms that made these medicines often took out a 'patent' to stop others copying their products. Some of the patent medicines contained dangerous substances like opium and alcohol. But it was much easier to buy something from the shop than to visit the doctor, and the shopkeepers often gave advice free.

Study the following sources and then use them together with your knowledge to answer the questions on page 53.

SOURCE 1 – Poor people can't afford doctors

The benefits of medicine as a trade will ever be confined to those who are able to pay for them, and of course the far great part of mankind will be everywhere deprived of them.

Dr William Buchan, *Domestic Medicine*, 15th edition, 1797

SOURCE 2 – The Lancaster Genuine Black Drop

This invaluable medicine is applicable in nervous affections, such as pains of the head and stomach, depression of mind, anxiety and irritability; in the gout, in wounds or inflammation; in chronic rheumatism; in coughs, asthmas and other complaints of the chest and in numerous diseases which produce pain and deprivation of sleep. At bed time six or eight drops to an adult and from one to three drops to a younger person.

Advertisement of John Braithwaite, Surgeon, of Lancaster, died 1810. The Black Drop was a mixture of opium and alcohol. Medicines of this sort were on sale in most English towns in the 19th century.

SOURCE 3 – Free medicine for some people

The people entitled to attendance are the poor inhabitants of Kendal, unable to purchase medicines, and who bring a ticket of admission from any subscriber [a wealthy local person who gave money to the dispensary]. Such patients as are able to come to the dispensary are desired to attend at certain hours. Patients incapable of coming are visited by the physician, surgeon or apothecary at their place of abode.

	Patients admitted	Died	Expenses for medicine
1821	1,698	49	£128 10s 3d (£128.51)

Report of Dr Thomas Proudfoot on the health of the people of the town of Kendal 1822. The Kendal Dispensary was founded in 1782. The total population of Kendal in 1821 was 10,455.

SOURCE 4 – Home remedies c.1860

The village possessed one so-called midwife, a Mrs Lancolm, a very tall and stout woman who attended all cases, high and low. She certainly brought my sister into the world very successfully, and probably myself.

Large pitch plasters were stuck upon our chests at the beginning of cold weather, and remained there till spring, when their removal was a painful process. Spring was also the time for brimstone and treacle, cod-liver oil, castor oil and Gregory powders were used at all seasons. Our teeth and eyes were left to themselves. If a tooth had to be taken out it was done by Mr Higgins, a chemist in Stamford. Spectacles were never used by the young.

Mary Mablane, *What I Remember*, 1947. As Mary Marshall she was born in 1850, the daughter of a Lincolnshire clergyman. Brimstone and treacle, castor oil and Gregory powders were all laxatives.

SOURCE 5 – Accidental death

An enquiry was held on Tuesday at the Green Man Inn before Mr Coroner Chaston, into the death of Maggie Alderton aged 1 year 9 months, the child of Henry Wade, agricultural labourer.

The evidence of the mother showed that the deceased accidentally overturned upon herself a cup of hot soup, sustaining scalds from which she died 40 hours later. No medical man was called, but Mrs Brundish was sent for to charm the fire out of the deceased. She attended and repeated some words and passed her hands over the injured places. In the opinion of the parents good was done. The witness added that Mrs Brundish's powers was generally believed in the village. Mr W. Cuthbert, surgeon, having given evidence, a verdict of 'accidental death' was returned.

Suffolk Times and Mercury, 16 December 1892

SOURCE 6 – Most people could not afford the doctor

When I was a child there was no National Health Service. People paid into sick clubs. Miners had 2 pence (1p) a week stopped from their pay to pay for doctors if they were ill. Medicine had to cost no more than 2d. Even so most people could not afford the doctor's fees and so they treated themselves. For sprains and bruises we fermented wild plants like comfrey and dog standard. For confinements we had to pay the doctor £1 1s (£1.05) or a neighbour could help out. That was all right when there were no complications. I fell off a wall and hurt my right knee and the pain settled on my hip. The doctor said I had a hip joint disease and wanted to send me to hospital. My mother did not want me to go so the doctor said he would treat me at home but we must pay 3s 6d (17.5p) each time he came. He would paint my hip with iodine one week and the next he would put a plaster on it. This made a big blister come up which he then pricked to let the fluid out. I did not walk for almost a year. I have often thought what a sacrifice my parents must have made to pay for the doctor when my father's wage was only one sovereign and one shilling (£1.05) a week.

Memories of Lily Horbury, 1974, of her childhood in a Yorkshire village, c.1900. Iodine is an antiseptic based on a chemical discovered in 1812.

SOURCE 7

Medicine advertisement from the *Illustrated London News*, 1891. Thomas Beecham was a Lancashire shopkeeper who made a fortune from pills. They contained ginger, aloes (a bitter fruit-juice) and soap, which cost less than 1 per cent of the price of the pills. Beecham had factories in the USA and other countries when he died in 1907.

SOURCE 8 – My mother was a marvellous midwife

Of course there was no help in those days, it was all home nursing and no hospitals. It's all so different now. They just used to send for her (my mother). I used to watch her bring the baby into the world and cut the cord. I know I wasn't very old but I was quite capable. I could now if necessary. She was a marvellous midwife. I'd go with her and rub their backs and keep them walking. It was important to keep them walking to speed up labour.

Mrs Coker Lambeth, London, Reminiscences of the 1890s, recorded 1980.

QUESTIONS

1. Make a list of the ways shown in the sources on pages 52-53 by which ordinary people in 19th-century Britain got medical help.

2. Which of the items in your list do you consider to have been most important? Explain your answer.

3. Study Source 1. Do the other sources on page 52 support Dr Buchan's view? Explain your answer with reference to the sources.

4. Study Source 5. 'Medical charms like that used by Mrs Brundish had been used since the Stone Age. This proves they must have worked.' Do you agree? What other explanation for their continued use can you suggest?

5. Study Source 7. 'Beecham's success proves that his pills must have worked.' Do you agree? What other explanation for his success can you suggest?

6. How useful as historical evidence are the memories of old people like those in sources 4, 6 and 8? Is their interpretation of events likely to be reliable?

7. Look back at pages 38-51. Which of the new medical developments discussed there made a real difference to the health of ordinary people in the 19th century? Explain your answer.

8. Use the sources on pages 52-53 and your own knowledge to answer the question 'Did the medical developments of the years 1500-1900 make important improvements in the medical care of ordinary people in 19th-century Britain?'

CHANGES AND DEVELOPMENTS 1500–1900: SUMMARY

The drawings below show some of the main changes that took place in medicine between 1500 and 1900,

KEY QUESTIONS
◆ *What changes took place?*
◆ *Which aspects of medicine stayed the same?*
◆ *Why had things changed or stayed the same?*
◆ *Had these changes taken place quickly or slowly?*

It was in Europe and North America that the rapid changes in medicine had taken place in the years 1500–1900. In the rest of the world things had often been influenced by events in Europe, but otherwise the traditional medicine had not changed very much.

1500   1900

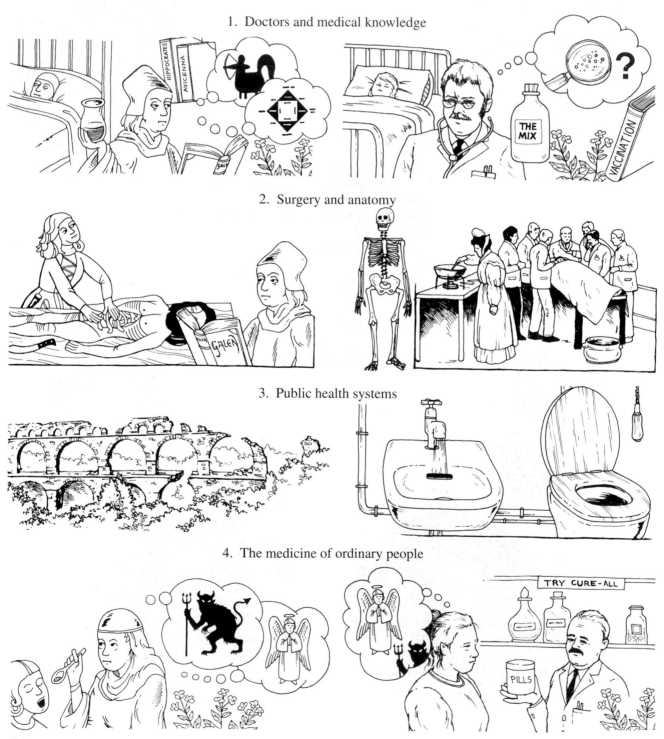

1. Doctors and medical knowledge

2. Surgery and anatomy

3. Public health systems

4. The medicine of ordinary people

William Harvey

Edward Jenner

Andreas Vesalius

Louis Pasteur

Famous individuals in history

◆ Why is each of these people famous?
◆ There is only one woman in this group; why?
◆ How important was science to each of these people?
◆ Which of these people built on the work of others?
◆ Which of these people overturned the work of others?
◆ Which of these people did things that directly helped sick people?
◆ Does this mean that these people were more important than the others?

Florence Nightingale

Robert Koch

Joseph Lister

James Simpson

HIGH-TECHNOLOGY MEDICINE

KEY QUESTIONS
- ◆ *How has 20th-century technology brought improvements in medicine?*
- ◆ *Are there any problems with high-technology medicine?*

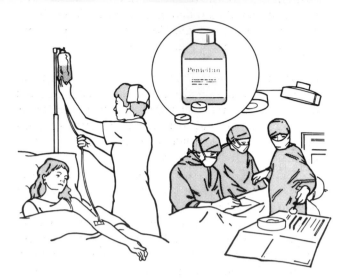

By 'high-technology medicine' we mean medicine that relies on the new machines, new chemicals and new skills of the 20th century.

In 1900 the development of science and technology had recently given doctors several new weapons, such as anaesthetics and antiseptics. In the 20th century it has given them many more:
- new drugs like penicillin
- new techniques, like blood transfusion
- new methods of surgery, like heart transplants.

There is nothing new about doctors making use of technology – for instance they have relied on skilled metal workers for knives for over 3000 years. But in the 20th century many doctors have come to rely on technology more than ever before.

Stopping the germs

By 1900 the scientists, using the work of Pasteur and Koch, could recognise the germs of some diseases and knew how to look for more. Research laboratories in universities and in industry in all the rich countries set out to look for them and to find ways to kill them.

One new development helped 20th-century scientists to identify more and more germs. In 1931 the electron microscope was invented. The germs causing many of the major diseases are too small to be seen with earlier microscopes. Now that they could be seen vaccines or anti-toxins could be developed to fight against them. By the 1950s scientists had found the germs that caused most of the major infectious diseases.

For some of these they found a vaccine that stopped people catching it, as Jenner's vaccine stopped them catching smallpox. For other diseases, animals could be used to produce a protective anti-toxin, as Behring had done for diphtheria in 1891.

SOURCE 1

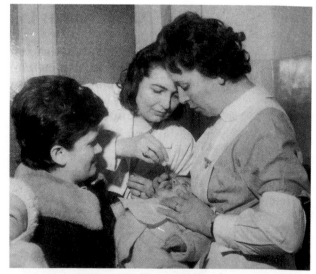

Vaccines stop people catching diseases. In 1954 the American Jonas Salk produced a vaccine that gave protection against the paralysing disease, polio. This picture shows a baby being given the vaccine in 1961.

◀ If the scientists had been law-men in the Wild West, they might have issued posters like this.

A magic bullet The anti-toxins are chemicals produced in the bodies of animals. One of Behring's students, Paul Ehrlich, wondered if man-made chemicals could be found that would work inside the body in the same way. 'We must learn to shoot microbes with magic bullets,' he said.

In Germany, where Ehrlich worked, the chemical industry was large and wealthy and ready to spend money on research that might find new uses for its products. Koch had used chemical dyes to stain microbes so that he could study them, and he found that some of them killed the microbes. What if there was one that would kill disease microbes without causing harm to the human body? Ehrlich could see how important this would be and in 1899 he set out to look for it. The search took him ten years. By 1909 he and his assistants had tried 605 different dyes on the germ of the disease syphilis, but without success. The 606th one worked. It killed the germ and cured the disease. The first 'magic bullet' had been found. It was called salvarsan.

Sulphonamides It was over twenty years before the second 'magic bullet' was discovered. In 1932 Gerhard Domagk, a scientist working for a large German chemical firm, discovered a dye that could kill the germs of several diseases without harming the human body. Then in 1935 French scientists found that it was one of a group of chemicals called the sulphonamides. Domagk had first used it to save the life of his daughter Hildegarde, who had pricked herself with a needle and had developed blood poisoning. But sulphonamides were soon found to cure many infectious diseases such as pneumonia and scarlet fever.

Penicillin The most important of the 'magic bullets' is probably penicillin, which can kill a wide range of germs inside the human body. In 1928 Alexander Fleming, a London bacteriologist, noticed in his laboratory that a mould called penicillium produced a substance that killed germs. He could see that it might be important, and in 1929 he wrote an article about it. But an enormous amount of research was needed to make and test the pure substance, penicillin. It was not until 1939 that a research team, led by Howard Florey at Oxford, began to work on it, just as the Second World War was beginning. In 1940 they proved that it worked and could kill a variety of germs inside the body, including those that caused blood poisoning in war wounds. A determined effort was made to produce it in quantity and by 1943 it began to save lives.

❖ *Between 1929 and 1939 little research was done on penicillin. Why was so much done in the years 1939–43?*

SOURCE 3 – Normally he would have died

We had enormous numbers of infected wounded, terrible burn cases among the crews of the armoured cars. Sulphonamides had absolutely no effect on these cases. The last thing I tried was penicillin. I had very little penicillin, something like 10 000 units, maybe less.

The first man I tried it on was a young New Zealand officer called Newton. He had been in bed for six months with compound fractures of both legs. His sheets were soaked with pus and the heat in Cairo made the smell intolerable. Normally he would have died in a short time. I gave three injections a day of penicillin and studied the effects under a microscope. The thing seemed like a miracle. In ten days time the left leg was cured and in a month's time the young fellow was back on his feet. I had enough penicillin left for ten cases. Nine of them were complete cures.

Lt Col. Pulvertaft, an army doctor in North Africa 1943, quoted in André Maurois, *Life of Sir Alexander Fleming*, 1959.

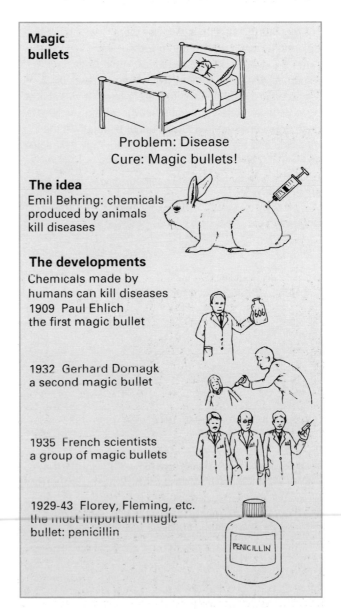

Magic bullets

Problem: Disease
Cure: Magic bullets!

The idea
Emil Behring: chemicals produced by animals kill diseases

The developments
Chemicals made by humans can kill diseases
1909 Paul Ehlich
the first magic bullet

1932 Gerhard Domagk
a second magic bullet

1935 French scientists
a group of magic bullets

1929-43 Florey, Fleming, etc.
the most important magic bullet: penicillin

PENICILLIN

VICTORIES FOR SCIENTIFIC MEDICINE

Since the 1940s many other drugs have been found that can tackle a wide range of germs inside the body. These discoveries add up to a revolution in the work of doctors.

Since the 1880s bacteriologists have been able to identify the germs causing most (but not all) of the infectious diseases. Since the 1930s doctors have been able to kill them or to prevent them spreading inside the body. Many problems remain – for instance bacteria resistant to the new drugs have developed and new forms of penicillin and other drugs have to be produced all the time to keep up. But the change brought about by the new drugs has been very great.

SOURCE 1 – A real revolution in medicine

For most of the infectious diseases there was nothing to be done beyond bed rest and good nursing care. Then came the start of the real revolution in medicine. I remember the astonishment when the first cases of septicaemia (blood poisoning) were treated. It was almost beyond belief. Here were patients who would surely have died, improving within a few hours of being given the medicine and feeling extremely well within the next day or so.

Lewis Thomas, *The Youngest Science*, 1985. Dr Thomas was a hospital doctor in the 1930s.

SOURCE 2

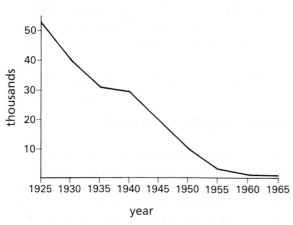

Deaths of people aged 0–44 from infectious diseases, 1925–1965. From A. Norton, *New Dimensions of Medicine*, 1969.

❖ *What other factors as well as new drugs might explain the change shown on this graph?*

SOURCE 3– New treatment for skin infections in the tropics

Superficial fungal infections pose a problem in the tropics, where the condition may be chronic and recurring. Over half of the patients in this study had suffered with their condition for six months or longer and many had received previous unsuccessful treatment.

Once-a-day application of 1 per cent bifonazole cream for 14 days produced a cure rate of 100 per cent with most conditions and 90 per cent of other more inaccessible complaints. The cream was well tolerated and caused no adverse reactions or allergy in any patients.

In conclusion, bifonazole seems an effective form of treatment for superficial fungal infections in the tropics and has the advantage of once-daily application, making patient compliance more likely.

Current Medical Research and Opinion, 1987, volume 10, page 390. Article by Femi Soyinka, a doctor in Ife, Nigeria, describing an improved treatment for complaints found particularly in the Nigerian climate.

SOURCE 4 – Modern treatment for leukaemia may lead to cure

Before modern treatment was available, acute lymphoblastic leukaemia in children under 12 years would certainly lead to death within three months. With present treatment with drugs and irradiation, 90 per cent of children will survive for three or more years before relapse and over one third will be permanently cured of the disease.

Compiled from current medical textbooks. Leukaemia is a cancer of the tissues that produce blood.

SOURCE 5 – A century of progress in combatting yellow fever

Yellow fever was responsible for several epidemics among the settlers in tropical areas of the Americas and Africa during the 17th to the 19th centuries. Scientific research into its cause and spread was started at the beginning of this century and progressed well ahead of other viral disease research. A safe and efficient vaccine was introduced in the 1940s and since then little progress has been made concerned with treatment. However, recent breakthroughs in the molecular study of the virus should provide new tools for further progress in treatment and control of the disease.

P.L.J. Bres, *Bulletin of the World Health Organisation*, 1986, volume 64, page 775. Yellow fever, like malaria, is spread by mosquitos, so the battle against the disease is both against the insect and against the virus.

Some new drugs have harmful effects

The new drugs were powerful weapons against disease. But powerful weapons can do harm as well as good. Since the 1940s many powerful new drugs have been developed, mainly by the firms that make and sell them. Some of these have turned out to do people very serious damage. Others can be harmful if wrongly used.

The cartoon (Source 6) makes a joke about the unexpected effects drugs can have. But these side-effects can be very serious (see Sources 7 and 9).

Thalidomide In 1961 a German drug firm produced a new drug that was very effective as a 'tranquilliser' – it calmed people's nerves and helped them to relax. The firm checked that it was not poisonous but they did not check for possible effects on unborn babies. Many thousands of pregnant women used the drug, and it was not until their babies were born that its full effects were seen – they had very badly deformed arms and legs, or none at all.

Over 6000 people are seriously disabled as a result of this drug, most of them in Germany, but some in other countries. Partly as a result of the thalidomide tragedy, stricter laws were passed in many countries to control the sale of drugs.

SOURCE 6

"DRUGS, SIDE-EFFECTS, MORE DRUGS, MORE SIDE-EFFECTS — COULDN'T I GO BACK TO THE ORIGINAL COLD?"

SOURCE 7

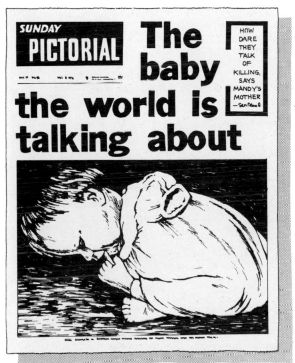

SOURCE 8 – 9000 new drugs

More than 9000 new drugs (have been developed) in the last 25 years. These drugs present new hazards as well as greater benefits than ever before – for they are widely used, they are often very potent and they are presented by aggressive sales campaigns that may tend to overstate their merits and fail to indicate the risks involved in their use.

President Kennedy, Message to US Congress 1962, asking for laws to control drug sales.

SOURCE 9 – Drug damages the brain

Powerful tranquillisers such as Largactil, which is used to deaden the emotions of mentally ill patients in prison hospitals, should be banned, the World Health Congress was told in Brighton today. More than 25 million patients have suffered irreversible brain damage as a result of the drugs, said Dr David Hill, senior clinical psychologist at the Walton Hospital, Chesterfield.

Roche, the main manufacturers, calculate that 150 million people in the world are taking the drugs, and 3 to 6 per cent may have harmful effects.

Independent studies had shown that one in four of the patients given the drug suffered, Dr Hill told the Congress.

Guardian, 16 July 1985

HIGH-TECHNOLOGY SURGERY

The advanced science and technology of the 20th century was of great help to the surgeons. New materials – rubber, stainless steel, plastics – made it easier to keep the operating theatre sterile (free of germs). Electricity was just coming into use so electrical machines could be made for X-rays and other purposes. Improvements in chemistry meant better anaesthetics.

Blood transfusion becomes possible   Surgeons have always faced three main problems: pain, infection and loss of blood. The first two had been solved by 1900, although further improvements in anaesthetics and antiseptics were still to come. But the answer to the third problem was found only in 1901.

As early as 1667 people had tried to replace lost blood with the blood of a healthy person. Sometimes this succeeded, but sometimes the blood clotted and killed the patient. In 1901 it was discovered that human blood falls into four main groups, and that only some of these can be mixed together safely. During the First World War methods of storing blood were developed and in most rich countries reserve stocks or 'blood banks' were set up in the 1940s and 1950s. By then blood transfusion was safe and easy and saved many lives.

❖ *What medical discovery of the 19th century had to be made before blood transfusion could be safe?*

SOURCE 1

A direct transfusion of blood 1837. A contemporary drawing. A safe method of blood transfusion was not discovered until the 20th century.

Machines to help the surgeons   Until the 20th century surgeons had to guess what had happened inside the body from what they could see or feel from the outside. In 1895 Wilhelm Röntgen discovered electro-magnetic radiation, which could pass through the human body. These 'X-rays' were used to look at broken bones as early as 1896. Later, methods were found to X-ray the soft parts of the

body as well, so that surgeons using X-rays could see clearly what was wrong before beginning an operation.

Many other electrical machines have been developed to help surgeons and other doctors. Some help them to find out what is wrong – for example the ECG machine, which records the electric current in the heart. Some can take over from part of the body and keep the patient alive – for example the kidney machine or the heart-lung machine.

SOURCE 2

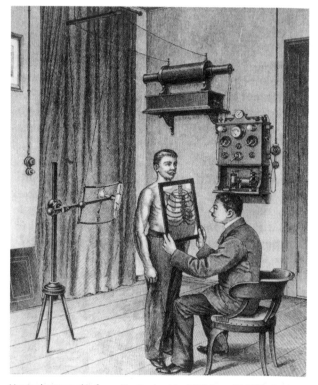

X-ray photograph of a patient's chest in 1903 from M. Wilhelm Meyer, *Die Naturkräfte*.

SOURCE 3

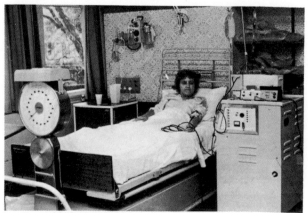

A patient with damaged kidneys receiving treatment with a kidney dialysis machine, which purifies her blood 1986.

. . . On Sunday his Majesty the King (Edward VII) experienced considerable pain. On Tuesday morning a consultation was held at which Lord Lister, Sir Thomas Smith and Sir Frederick Treves were present. The opinion was unanimous that an immediate operation was an absolute necessity. But we feel justified in saying that should no complication arise His Majesty may be restored to health and live for many years to occupy the throne.

British Medical Journal, 5 July 1902. The operation was successful and Edward VII lived until 1910, when he died at the age of 68.

❖ *What effect would this operation on the king have on the development of surgery of this type?*

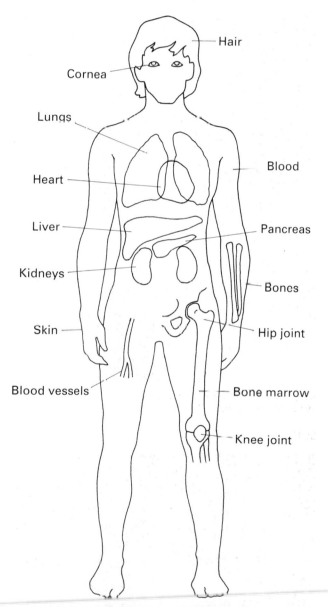

Parts of the human body that can be transplanted from one person to another or replaced artificially.

Some successes of high-technology surgery

The new methods made surgery much safer and opened up new possibilities. Operations deep inside the body, like that to remove a diseased appendix, became reliable and safe. This operation was first carried out in 1886.

By the 1960s surgeons could even replace some damaged organs with healthy ones given by other people. The first heart transplant was made in 1967 by Dr Christiaan Barnard, in South Africa.

In the 1970s and 1980s operations were developed to replace hip joints and many other body parts with artificial substitutes. In the 1990s came 'key-hole surgery' in which the surgeon sends the instruments in through a tiny hole in the body, and controls them by watching a TV screen. This is less of a shock for the patient, so he or she can go home days sooner and recover quickly.

SOURCE 5 – We used all the techniques of modern medicine

As soon as we had Louis Washkansky in our ward, we had to know everything about him. We used all the techniques of modern medicine to spy on the hidden interior of the human body. Kidney function was checked, by measuring its urine output. The liver was studied through urine and blood analysis. The heart pattern was plotted by electrocardiogram. The lungs were X-rayed. Blood chemistry was checked in the laboratory.

The average person is estimated to have 60 000 microbes on each square inch of skin. Perhaps the most dangerous were the enemies harboured within the body. We took samples from the skin, nose, throat, mouth and rectum. All members of staff who were to look after the patient also had their noses, throats and rectums studied.

So the long wait began. Some day, we knew, one of the screaming ambulances would come up the hill bringing a dying human being – with an uninjured heart. Louis Washkansky lay in my ward three weeks waiting for a donor. Then, shortly after eight o'clock one night, the phone rang. . . .

There were two operations, not one. We needed two teams of men and women. One would hold in life the vital organs of the donor while the other prepared Louis Washkansky. A single error on either side would collapse the whole operation.

Christiaan Barnard, *Christiaan Barnard: One Life,* 1969. The operation was on 3 December 1967. It succeeded but 18 days later Washkansky died. In 1984 the longest surviving heart transplant patient had lived 15 years after his operation.

SOURCE 1

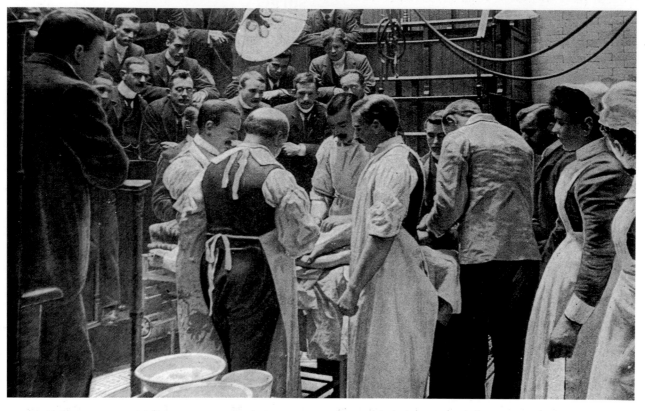

Above Charing Cross Hospital, London, 1901. Surgery was antiseptic – every effort was made to kill germs on or near the open wound.

Below St Stephen's Hospital, London 1988. In the 20th century aseptic surgery meant the entire operating theatre was kept as germ free as possible.

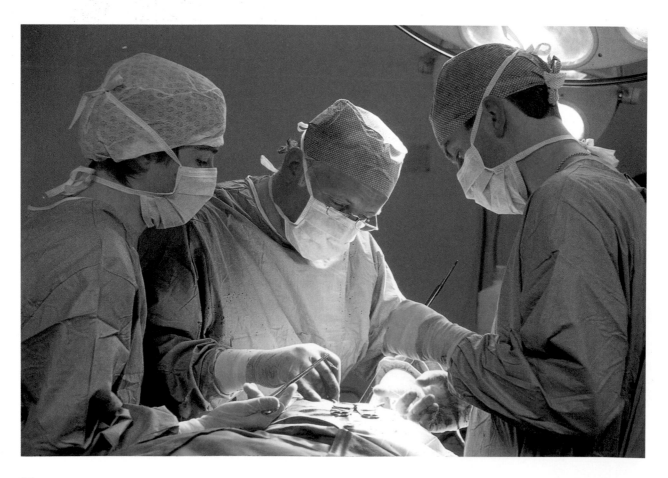

Some problems of high-technology surgery

Mistakes can be very serious   Doctors and nurses have made mistakes at all periods of history. In the complicated operations of modern surgery there are many things that can go wrong, and some occasionally do. Even a fairly simple mistake can have disastrous results for the patient (see Source 3).

Who is to decide?   An operation like a heart transplant takes up so many doctors and others that not many operations can be done. So the doctors have to decide who is to have one, and who is perhaps to be left to die. There is a similar problem if someone is in a coma for a long time. They are kept alive, using a special machine, and the doctor may have to decide when the patient is really dead and the machine can be switched off.

Cost   The teams of doctors and nurses needed for modern surgery can only work in a large and well-equipped hospital. This might cost at least £50 million to build and £80 000 a year for each bed to run (1995 prices). A single heart transplant could cost about £25 000. In earlier periods of history medical care was mainly paid for by the patients or by their families. Who was to pay for the expensive new high-technology medicine of the 20th century?

SOURCE 3 – Blood transfusion with tainted blood. Boy dies of AIDS

Stephen Gaudin, a 15-year-old French boy has died of AIDS-induced septicaemia. He wrote a moving book about living with AIDS after receiving a contaminated blood transfusion eight years ago.

His younger brother Laurent, whose slow death filmed by their father moved millions of TV viewers to tears, died in 1991 aged 11. Both boys were infected by blood products that have contaminated 1250 haemophiliacs and have killed more than 11 so far. Four senior public health officials accused of knowingly allowing AIDS-tainted blood to be given to haemophiliacs [because it was cheaper] are on trial.

'I am crushed. 18 months ago we were a family of five. Now three are left,' M. Gaudin told Le Parisien. 'Both my sons died because of money. I shall never accept it.'

The Times, 4th June 1993

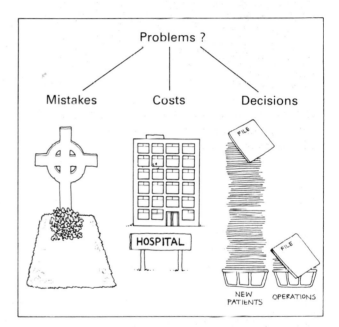

The cost of the British National Health Service. Since the NHS only started in 1948 there are no earlier figures for comparison.

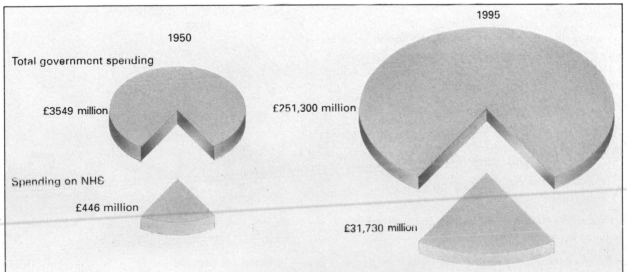

GOVERNMENTS AND HEALTH CARE

KEY QUESTIONS
- ◆ *How have British governments in the 20th century tried to improve the health of the people?*
- ◆ *Why have they done this?*

By 1900 the governments of most rich countries like Britain accepted that it was part of their job to organise a good public health system, with pure water and effective sewers. But they considered that the rest of health care was a matter for people to organise privately for themselves, paying fees to doctors or hospitals when they needed them. This meant that many people did without.

During the 20th century governments of many countries have begun to take a much more active part in organising doctors and hospitals and caring for personal health. This has varied from country to country. For instance in the USA the government has still left nearly all health care in private hands, whereas in the Soviet Union under communism it was all controlled by the government. Britain comes in between the two.

The growth of the British health services Many people had opposed the Public Health Acts of the 19th century. People continued to oppose the new health services of the 20th century. But as you can see from the diagram, from 1900 onwards the governments accepted more and more new tasks. They did this for a number of reasons:

1. Because they could see that poverty was the cause of much ill health. So by tackling poverty they might prevent the ill health.

❖ *Which of the reforms in the diagram might improve health by tackling poverty?*

2. Another factor that may explain the coming of so many new health services is the reform of Parliament. In 1918 and 1928 everybody over 21, including women for the first time, gained the right to vote.

❖ *How might this lead to health reforms?*

3. In this period Britain was involved in three major wars:
   The Boer War 1899–1902
   The First World War 1914–18
   The Second World War 1939–45

❖ *How might these wars influence the developments shown in the diagram?*

❖ *Which of the developments shown might help to make expensive high-technology medicine available to everyone?*

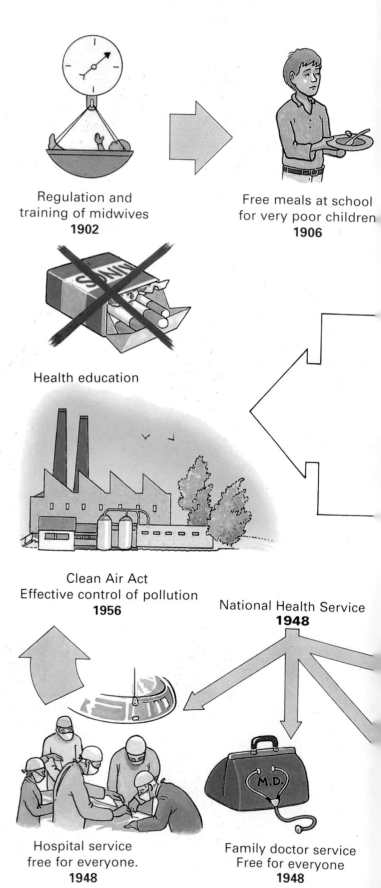

Regulation and training of midwives **1902**

Free meals at school for very poor children **1906**

Health education

Clean Air Act Effective control of pollution **1956**

National Health Service **1948**

Hospital service free for everyone. **1948**

Family doctor service Free for everyone **1948**

Government and public health in Britain since 1900

This chart does not show the old systems, like water supply and sewage disposal, that were already in existence in 1900.

National Insurance
1911

Sick pay and cost of doctors and medicines (not hospitals) for wage earners only (not dependents)

Health visitors to see and advise every new mother
1907

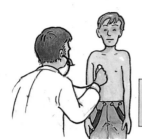

Medical inspection at school
1907

Old age pension (for over 70s)
1908

Unemployment pay

Government and local councils

Free inoculations and vaccinations for:
(smallpox since 1853)
Diphtheria 1940
Tuberculosis 1948
Triple vaccine 1954
(diphtheria, whooping cough and tetanus)
Polio 1955
Measles 1946
German measles 1969

Medical Research Council
1911

Council house building and slum clearance
1919+

Town planning
1948

Free for everyone 1948–51, then some pay part of the cost.

Medicine
1948

1948
National Insurance for everyone
– sick pay
– unemployment pay
– maternity benefit
– death benefit
– pension

Clinics to treat babies and children usually free
1919+

Dental service
1948

Family allowances
1948

Social services
1948

Some councils run hospitals
1929

WAR PROMPTS HEALTH REFORMS

The third factor that we suggested to explain why governments took action to improve health was war. During the First World War, for instance, the heroes were the ordinary soldiers who had lived through the horrors of trench warfare. When the war ended in 1918 the Government promised that it would provide 'Homes fit for heroes to live in.' The diagram on page 65 shows one way in which they tried to keep this promise.

The Second World War had a more direct effect on health services. When the war began in 1939 there was no National Health Service. Those who could afford to pay for a doctor or for medical treatment could get it easily. Those who could not often did without. There was no blood transfusion service or ambulance service in most areas.

The Government could see that it would be quite impossible to fight the war unless things were better organised. They expected thousands of people to be injured in air raids, and they knew that people needed good health to work hard in the war factories as well as to fight. So at the beginning of the war all the hospitals were brought under government orders,

a national blood transfusion service was set up, ambulance services were organised everywhere, and free or cheap medical service was provided for all who needed it. Politicians had been arguing about the need for many of these things for years. Now there was a war there was no time to argue, and nobody did.

The emergency system worked well during the war, and the health of the nation was better than in peacetime. What would happen when the war ended?

❖ *If any political party suggested going back to the old pre-war system, who would have voted for them?*

In fact all the parties agreed that there had to be a National Health Service, though they disagreed about the details. In 1948 the Labour Government brought it into existence. Since then it has grown very much in size, but otherwise has not changed very much.

❖ *What are the main differences between the NHS and the earlier health services shown on the diagram (pages. 64–65)?*

SOURCE 1

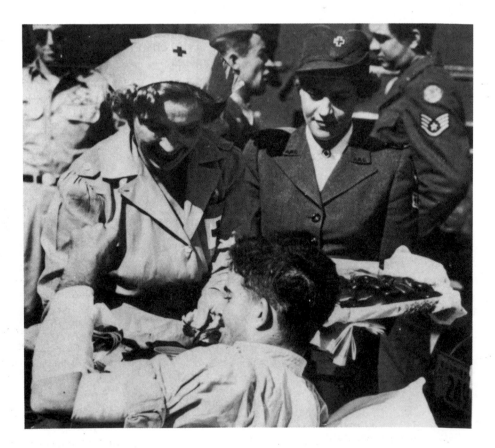

A soldier being tended by a nurse in the Second World War.

Some improvements: why did they happen?

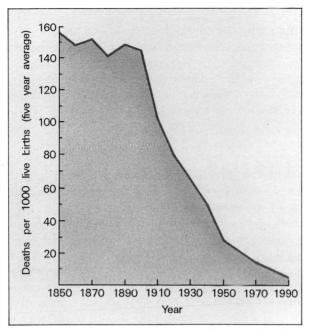

Graph 1 Deaths of children under the age of one year from all causes 1850–1990.

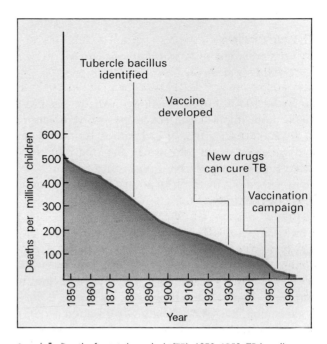

Graph 2 Deaths from tuberculosis (TB), 1850–1960. TB is a disease that weakens people for many years and may kill them. It spreads easily in bad housing conditions. Healthy and well-fed people are less likely to be seriously affected.

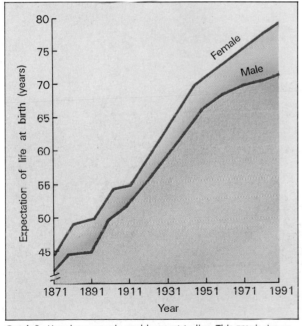

Graph 3 How long people could expect to live. This graph shows to what average age a baby born at various dates could be expected to live.

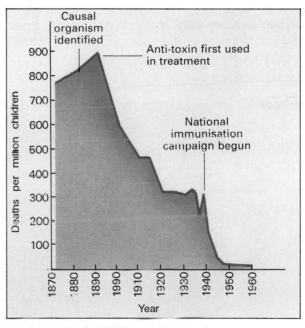

Graph 4 Deaths from diphtheria, a highly infectious disease. Healthy well-fed children were much more likely to recover than sickly and badly fed ones.

In the years covered by these graphs three factors worked together to improve health in England and Wales.
1. High technology medicine came into use.
2. Governments came to play a much greater part in health care.
3. The standard of living in England and Wales improved greatly for most people.

❖ *How might high-technology medicine have affected the changes shown on these graphs?*
❖ *Which of the government actions mentioned on pages 64–65 might have affected these changes?*
❖ *How might the rising standard of living have affected these changes?*
❖ *Is it possible to say that any one of these three factors was more important than the others?*

67

HEALTH FOR ALL

KEY QUESTION

◆ *Does everyone in the world now use high-technology medicine?*

Since the 1940s, high-technology medicine has had a much more important effect in the poorer countries of Asia and Africa than it had earlier. As new drugs and vaccines came into use in the rich countries, infectious diseases like diphtheria or polio were being wiped out there. Why not try to do the same in the poor countries?

Until the 1940s and 1950s many of these countries had been ruled over by Europeans as parts of their empires. Now they gained their independence, and set up their own governments. These were anxious to improve health services, and in 1948 a new organisation, the World Health Organisation (WHO), was set up to help them.

The World Health Organisation WHO is part of the United Nations Organisation, to which most nations belong. Its main task is to develop the health services of all nations, but especially of the poorer ones that need help most. WHO sends expert advisers and pays for the training and equipment of health workers in the poor countries.

SOURCE 1 – The right to health

The enjoyment of the highest attainable standard of health is one of the fundamental rights of every human being without distinction of race, religion, political belief, economic or social condition.

Constitution of WHO, 1948

Attacks on infectious diseases WHO has helped many countries to start and run programmes of vaccinations or campaigns to get rid of diseases carried by insects. In 1955 it began an attempt, so far unsuccessful, to wipe out the most common tropical disease, malaria. In 1967 it tackled smallpox, this time with complete success. There have been no cases anywhere in the world since 1980.

SOURCE 2

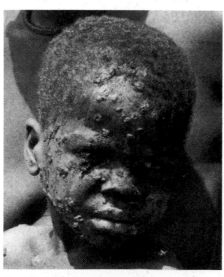

The little boy in the photograph above is five years old. He lives in a bush village in Nigeria. He has yaws, a disease which causes disfiguring and painful sores and which will continue for his lifetime if untreated. After the World Health Organisation team visited the village and gave him an injection of penicillin, the boy's sores had almost disappeared.

SOURCE 3

Family planning Partly because of the success of these health programmes the population of the poorer countries rose sharply. How could these extra people find work, food and housing? If they could not find them, how could they keep healthy? One answer to this problem was to encourage people to have smaller families.

SPACING BIRTHS REDUCES DEATH

Source : WHO survey of 6,000 women in a developing country

Births intervals in years	Deaths	Number of infant deaths (before age one) per 1000 live births
1		200
2		145
2-3		100
3-4		80

The picture above shows an ideal size family and the chart below emphasises the risks in having too many children. From *World Health*, June 1984, a magazine produced by WHO.

SOURCE 4 – Two billion people left out

Almost two billion people worldwide have no access to modern health care, according to estimates by the World Health Organisation. This may be because of the distance they live from such facilities or their inability to pay. Often people will turn for help first to a traditional medical practitioner. This is someone they respect, who acts as an interpreter of their beliefs about the origin of disease and who can suggest a treatment.

Guardian, 24 January 1995. The population of the world in 1995 was about 5.5 billion.

'Health For All by 2000' In 1981, 158 member countries of the World Health Organisation agreed to set 'Health for All' as a goal. WHO lists eight essentials as:

1. Education about health problems.
2. Promotion of food supply and proper nutrition.
3. Safe water and basic sanitation.
4. Maternal and child health care, including family planning.
5. Immunisation against the major infectious diseases.
6. Prevention and control of the main local diseases.
7. Treatment of common diseases and injuries.
8. Provision of essential drugs.

❖ *Of the eight suggestions of WHO:*
   a. Which depend on 'high-technology' medicine?
   b. Which depend on other changes in politics, farming or industry?
   c. Which depend on actions by governments?
   d. Which depend on actions by people themselves?

SOURCE 5

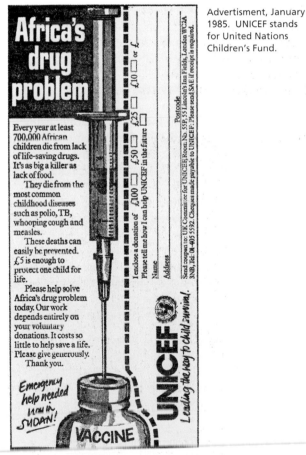

Advertisment, January 1985. UNICEF stands for United Nations Children's Fund.

OLDER MEDICAL IDEAS CONTINUE

KEY QUESTION
◆ *Does everyone in the world now use high-technology medicine?*

1. In Asia and Africa

While high-technology medicine was developing in Europe and America, the people of other parts of the world continued with their traditional systems. When Europeans came to conquer or to trade they usually brought European doctors with them, but the main work of these doctors was to look after the Europeans. A very few of them were medical missionaries who went there to help the local people for religious reasons. They usually gave treatment for nothing.

In most places, however, the local people naturally continued with their own traditional medicines. In many cases a traditional remedy worked perfectly well, perhaps better than a European one, and it was certain to be very much cheaper to make.

❖ *If such remedies worked why were they not widely used in the west?*

In China the traditional system of medicine was very well organised, though a few Chinese doctors had been trained in Europe or the USA. After the Chinese Revolution of 1949, the communist government began a determined policy of combining traditional Chinese medicine with scientific European ideas.

SOURCE 1 – Better within a week

I had two sand-fly bites on my ankle and instep. I scratched them and turned the spot into a quickly-growing ulcer. The standard European treatment was to burn the ulcer with carbon dioxide 'snow'. It was fiendishly painful and so was the condition. I could hardly hobble.

My Indian servant said to me, 'I could cure you quickly if you would let me use one of our remedies.' I agreed and he took the leaves of the Neem tree, mashed them up with some herby powder, made a square pad with a clean cloth and bound this over the wounds. Within a week my ulcers healed.

Of course the healing for me might have begun with the burning away of the infected flesh, or it might have been my own faith that the Indian remedy would work.

Memories of her life in India in the 1930s by Joan Brander, 1984

SOURCE 2

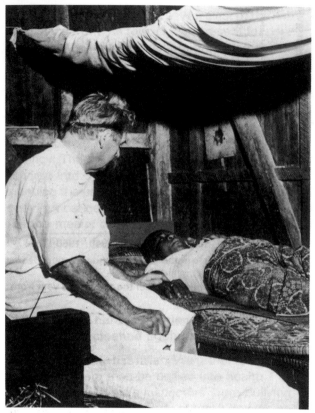

Dr Albert Schweitzer treating a patient in Gabon, then part of the French Empire. Schweitzer and his wife set up a hospital in Lambarene, Gabon, in 1913.

SOURCE 3 – Traditional methods tested

Sometimes traditional Chinese methods can treat an illness that modern medicine is incapable of dealing with. At other times the opposite is true, especially in those cases that require surgery or high-technology equipment.

In one experiment 62 patients with stomach ulcers were observed and evaluated by doctors trained in western methods, but treated by traditional Chinese methods.
    53 (81.5%) recovered
     7 (10.8%) showed some improvement
     2 (3.1%) showed no change

T.J. Kaptchuk, *Chinese Medicine*, 1983. Dr Kaptchuk is a Canadian doctor who studied Chinese medicine in China. He quotes the *Journal of Traditional Chinese Medicine,* 1959 for the experiment.

❖ *What other figures would you need to decide what these figures prove?*

SOURCE 4 – Traditional healers are very important

Many of the plants familiar to the 'witch doctor' really do have the healing power that tradition attaches to them. The ages-old arts of the herbalist must be tapped. There is no doubt that the judicious use of plants in health care can make a major contribution towards reducing a developing country's drugs bill. An army of traditional healers and herbalists can help to make attainable a goal of health care for all by the year 2000.

Dr Halfdan Mahler, Director of the World Health Organisation, *Guardian*, 16 May 1985.

SOURCE 5 – Traditional treatments work

Traditional medicine is very effective in calming agitated patients. I much prefer it to valium (a 'high-tech' drug used for the same purpose). It's very good for mental problems, but the kru (local traditional healers) also have treatments for physical problems, for example for infected joints, which really help.

Dr G. Wimhofer, a surgeon working in a Red Cross hospital in Thailand. The hospital is in a refugee camp, and works with a team of 20 traditional healers to care for 30 000 people. *Guardian*, 15 February 1985.

SOURCE 6 – Relaxed and awake while a lung is removed

It is an extraordinary experience to see a patient lying relaxed and awake, sipping tea, on an operating table, an acupuncturist twirling a needle about 2 inches long above her wrist, while a TB lung is being removed.

Professor S. Rosen, Mount Sinai School of Medicine, USA. Quoted in Brian Inglis, *Natural Medicine*, 1979.

2. In Europe and North America

In Europe and North America the coming of high-technology medicine in the 20th century did not mean that everybody stopped using remedies based on older ideas. People were used to discussing their ailments with friends and neighbours and buying medicines from the chemist's or from the herbalist's shop, where traditional remedies were still sold. Some of them still went to faith healers or tried 'nature cures' using diet and exercise.

Events like the thalidomide tragedy, which showed that high-technology medicine could go wrong, worried many people, and during the 1960s and 1970s more people turned to these 'alternative' sorts of medicine. One example is acupuncture. At this time there was plenty of evidence from China that acupuncture could be used as an alternative to anaesthetics.

Since about 1960 use of acupuncture has spread widely in the USA and in Europe. Doctors have no agreed scientific explanation of how it works, but they agree that it does, and some of them use it.

Most of the 'alternative' healers claimed that their remedies worked through using the natural powers of the patient's body or mind, but they could not show how. To many doctors these 'alternative' methods were out-of-date and unscientific. They felt that people who used them were 'quacks', just out to make money with cures that did no real good and might do harm. Despite this, according to a survey in 1981 there were in Britain about 30 000 'alternative practitioners'. Ten thousand of them were members of organised bodies like the National Institute of Medical Herbalists, and 2000 of them were also qualified doctors. About 10 million people were said to have consulted them. (The population of Britain in 1981 was 55.7 million.) Their numbers have grown considerably in the years since then.

❖ *Do these figures show*
  a. that 'alternative' methods must really work?
  b. that many people are easily taken in by 'quacks'?

SOURCE 7

This patient is undergoing a chest operation in Beijing, China, anaesthetised solely by an acupuncture needle in his left arm.

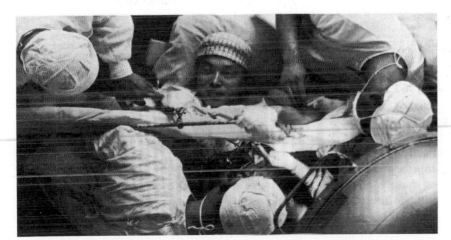

SOME NEW HEALTH PROBLEMS

KEY QUESTION
◆ *Has 20th-century medicine solved all our health problems?*

1. Smoking and health

By the later 20th century the battle against many of the infectious diseases had been won. Partly as a result of this, people were living much longer. But some diseases develop slowly and affect mainly middle-aged and elderly people. Now these diseases had a chance to develop and they became much more important.

The most serious killer diseases are now heart disease and cancer. High-technology surgery or drugs can help people who suffer from these diseases, but can be very expensive and can fail. Prevention would be much better, as it was with smallpox. But the problem is quite different from that of finding a vaccine against an infectious disease. Heart disease and cancer have many causes. For instance doctors think that heart disease can be caused by eating too much or eating the wrong foods, taking too little exercise, and smoking. So if people want to avoid heart disease as they get older they must avoid these habits earlier in life. All the doctors can do is explain the dangers as clearly as possible. They have done this most clearly in the case of lung cancer (see Source 1).

SOURCE 1 – Smoking is Britain's biggest killer

Lung cancer causes more deaths than any other type of cancer. A major cause of the disease is reliably known. Treatment fails in about 90 per cent of cases.

Thirty years of laboratory research has yet to identify the carcinogenic (cancer-causing) factors in cigarette smoke. It is difficult to explain the risks in a way that people will understand. How exactly this message should be put across is a matter of experiment. It may be helpful to make a comparison with other conditions, for example:

SMOKING IS BRITAIN'S BIGGEST KILLER

Among 1000 young adults who smoke cigarettes regularly:
>   about 1 will be murdered
>   about 6 will be killed on the roads
>   about 250 will be killed by tobacco.

Dr R. Peto and Dr R. Doll. *New Scientist*, 24 January 1985. Dr Peto and Dr Doll are leading cancer experts. In 1950 Dr Doll organised the research which first showed that cigarette smoking causes lung cancer. 40 000 doctors took part in the study.

❖ *What actions might help to cut down the number of people killed by heart disease and lung cancer:*
  a. actions by doctors
  b. actions by the government
  c. actions by people themselves?

What did people in Britain die of in 1992?

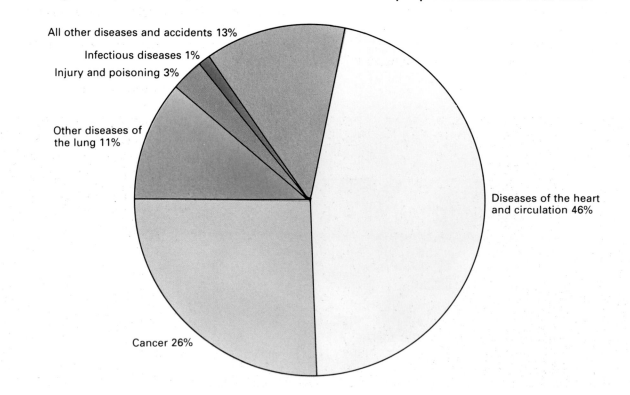

All other diseases and accidents 13%

Infectious diseases 1%

Injury and poisoning 3%

Other diseases of the lung 11%

Diseases of the heart and circulation 46%

Cancer 26%

2. AIDS

Just when it seemed that modern medicine had triumphed over most known serious diseases, AIDS appeared. AIDS is caused by a virus called HIV (Human Immunodeficiency Virus), which damages the body's defence system so that it cannot fight certain infections. It was first identified in 1981, although there had been cases before that. Thousands of people in Africa and the western world have died of AIDS/HIV. At the moment, there is no cure.

AIDS/HIV is transmitted through unprotected sex (not just between homosexuals), through sharing needles used in drug-taking, through haemophiliacs using infected blood and from an infected mother to her baby. The way people live in the late 20th century, far from stamping out the disease, has helped it to spread. In Africa, thousands of people have moved to big cities, away from their families, making casual sexual encounters more common. Inoculation programmes in Africa against other diseases have sometimes spread AIDS/HIV because needles have not been properly sterilised. People travel around the world easily, so the disease has become widespread. Blood transfusions can spread infected blood, especially where (in the USA for example) blood from paid donors is used.

Some of the panic reactions to AIDS/HIV have been very similar to the reactions of people to the Black Death in the 14th century. Many do not understand how AIDS/HIV is spread, and fear that it could be spread by touch, for example. In the USA policemen and firemen have asked to be issued with rubber gloves; funeral directors have refused to lay out the bodies of AIDS victims for burial; TV crews have refused to be in the same studio as people with AIDS/HIV. When President Clinton met a group of gays at the White House in 1995, the entire security staff wore rubber gloves.

Governments have been able to use 20th-century methods to try to educate people about AIDS/HIV. In Britain, leaflets were sent to every house in the country and all four TV channels have carried AIDS/HIV education programmes. Source 1 is from one of these leaflets. Source 2 is from a poster campaign designed to tell people that AIDS/HIV is not confined to young male gays.

❖ *Why would it have been unlikely for AIDS to have spread in the way it has if it had arisen fifty or a hundred years ago?*
❖ *Why have there been panic reactions to AIDS/HIV?*
❖ *Is it the government's job to publish leaflets and posters like Sources 1 and 2?*
❖ *Warning people how to avoid diseases is important. But many people have been against providing information about AIDS/HIV? Why?*
❖ *What 20th-century medical techniques are being used to try to remove or cure AIDS/HIV?*

SOURCE 1 – How HIV is not passed on

Everyday contact with someone who has HIV or AIDS is perfectly safe. The virus cannot be passed on through touching, shaking hands or hugging.
- You *cannot* be infected with HIV by touch, or sharing objects used by an infected person: cups, cutlery, glass, food, clothes, toilet seats and door-knobs.
- HIV cannot be passed on by sneezing or coughing.
- Swimming pools are safe too.
- HIV is not known to be passed on through tears or sweat.
- You cannot be infected with HIV by mosquitoes and other insects.

From a leaflet published by the Health Education Authority, 1990

SOURCE 2
Poster produced by the Health Education Authority

AIDS CAN AFFECT ANYONE

CHANGES AND DEVELOPMENTS 1900 – TODAY: SUMMARY

The drawings below show some of the main changes that took place in medicine in the 20th century.

KEY QUESTIONS
◆ *What changes took place?*
◆ *Which of the four areas of medicine shown here have changed the most?*
◆ *Which has changed the least?*

1900   **Today**

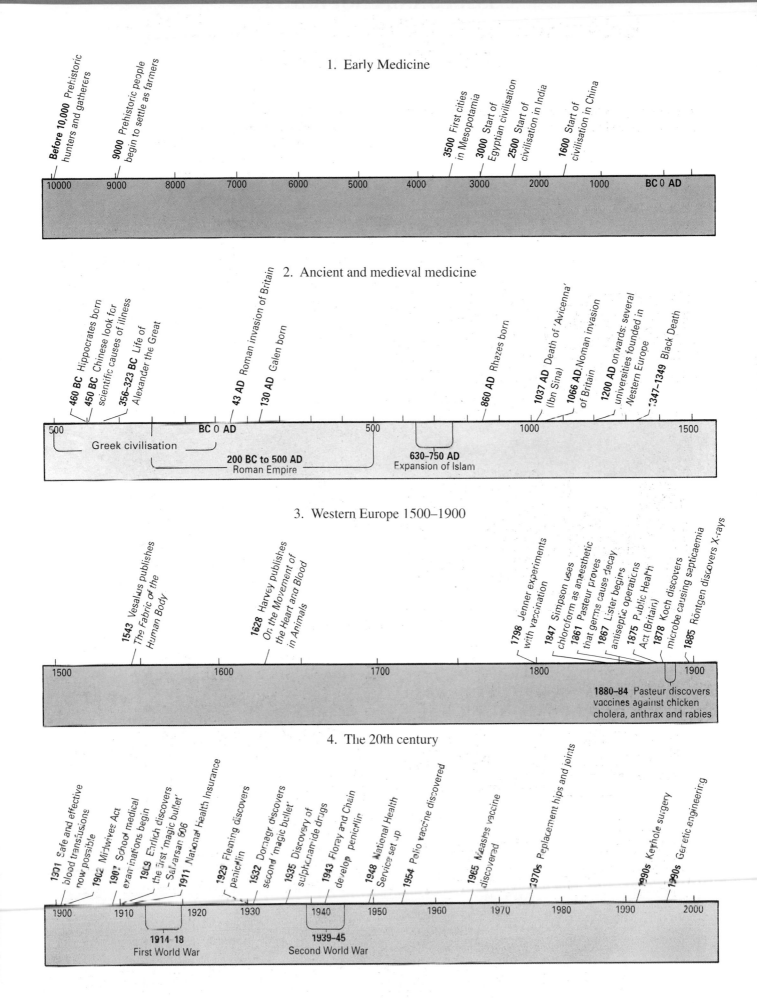

1. Early Medicine

Before 10,000 Prehistoric hunters and gatherers

9000 Prehistoric people begin to settle as farmers

3500 First cities in Mesopotamia

3000 Start of Egyptian civilisation

2500 Start of civilisation in India

1600 Start of civilisation in China

10000	9000	8000	7000	6000	5000	4000	3000	2000	1000	BC 0 AD

2. Ancient and medieval medicine

460 BC Hippocrates born

450 BC Chinese look for scientific causes of illness

356–323 BC Life of Alexander the Great

43 AD Roman invasion of Britain

130 AD Galen born

860 AD Rhazes born

1037 AD Death of 'Avicenna' (Ibn Sina)

1066 AD Norman invasion of Britain

1200 AD onwards: several universities founded in Western Europe

1347–1349 Black Death

| 500 | | BC 0 AD | | 500 | | 1000 | | 1500 |

Greek civilisation

200 BC to 500 AD Roman Empire

630–750 AD Expansion of Islam

3. Western Europe 1500–1900

1543 Vesalius publishes *The Fabric of the Human Body*

1628 Harvey publishes *On the Movement of the Heart and Blood in Animals*

1798 Jenner experiments with vaccination

1847 Simpson uses chloroform as anaesthetic

1861 Pasteur proves that germs cause decay

1867 Lister begins antiseptic operations

1875 Public Health Act (Britain)

1878 Koch discovers microbe causing septicaemia

1885 Röntgen discovers X-rays

| 1500 | | 1600 | | 1700 | | 1800 | | 1900 |

1880–84 Pasteur discovers vaccines against chicken cholera, anthrax and rabies

4. The 20th century

1901 Safe and effective blood transfusions now possible

1902 Midwives Act

1907 School medical examinations begin

1909 Ehrlich discovers the first 'magic bullet' – Salvarsan 606

1911 National Health Insurance

1928 Fleming discovers penicillin

1932 Domagk discovers second 'magic bullet'

1935 Discovery of sulphonamide drugs

1943 Florey and Chain develop penicillin

1948 National Health Service set up

1954 Polio vaccine discovered

1965 Measles vaccine discovered

1970s Replacement hips and joints

1990s Keyhole surgery

1990s Genetic engineering

| 1900 | 1910 | 1920 | 1930 | 1940 | 1950 | 1960 | 1970 | 1980 | 1990 | 2000 |

1914–18 First World War

1939–45 Second World War

WHY DO THINGS HAPPEN IN HISTORY?

Now you have looked at **The Story in Outline** you have begun to see what happened in the history of medicine. But historians are interested in more than what happened: they want to know why it happened.

In this first part of the **Issues and Enquiries** section of the book you will look at four factors which have often affected the history of medicine: religion; war; government action; science and technology.

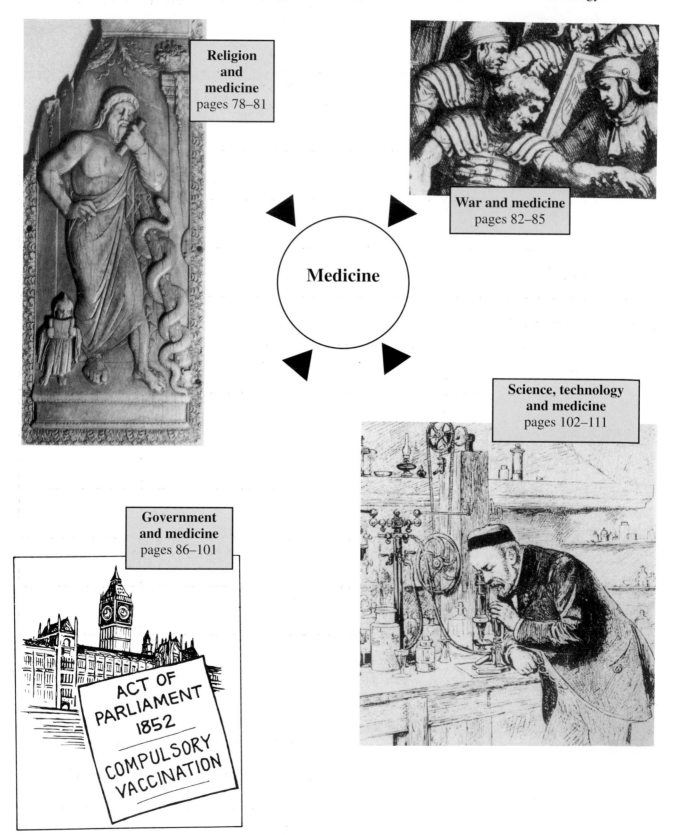

Religion and medicine
pages 78–81

War and medicine
pages 82–85

Medicine

Science, technology and medicine
pages 102–111

Government and medicine
pages 86–101

ACT OF PARLIAMENT 1852 COMPULSORY VACCINATION

Think back over what you know already about the history of medicine. When have religion, war, government action or science and technology affected medicine?

Did they cause change, or speed it up?
Did they stop change, or slow it down?

The table lists several sources from **The Story in Outline**.
Copy out the table.
In the first column write in the factor which the source is telling you about.
In the second column put + if the factor (or factors) is causing change or speeding it up.
Put – if it is stopping change or slowing it up.

	FACTOR	EFFECT
Page 10 Source 1		
Page 13 Source 6		
Page 18 Source 1		
Page 21 Source 5		
Page 24 Sources 1 and 2		
Page 24 Source 3		
Page 29 Source 3		
Page 43 Source 2		
Page 56 Source 1		
Page 62 Source 2		
Page 70 Source 2		

❖ *Did each factor start new changes or speed up existing ones?*
❖ *Did it slow down changes or prevent them?*
❖ *Were there times when it had little effect?*
❖ *How important was the factor in the history of medicine?*

1 RELIGION AND MEDICINE

KEY QUESTIONS

◆ *How has religion encouraged medical change?*

◆ *How has religion opposed change?*

◆ *Have there been times when religion was a factor of special importance or of little importance?*

In most periods of history, people's religious beliefs have strongly influenced their ideas about medicine. Sometimes the religious factor has encouraged new developments and sometimes it has worked against them.

The time chart shows some of the ways in which religion has influenced medical ideas. Some of these have been described in the previous section **The Story in Outline**. Some are described in sources on the next three pages.

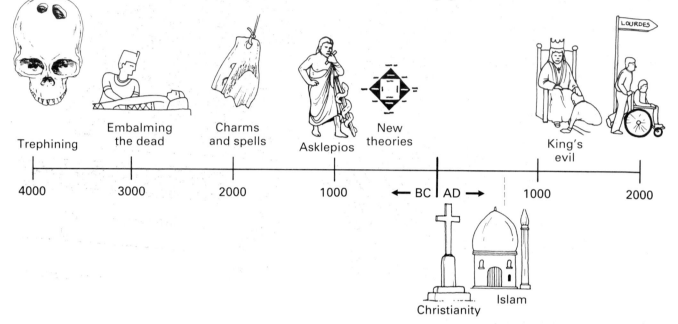

Trephining 4000 | Embalming the dead 3000 | Charms and spells 2000 | Asklepios 1000 | New theories ← BC | AD → Christianity | Islam | King's evil 1000 | 2000

SOURCE 1 – In the temple of Asklepios

First we had to bathe Plutus (a blind man) in the sea. Then we entered the temple where we placed our offerings to the gods on the altar. Soon the temple priest put out the light and told us to go to sleep and not to speak, no matter what noises we heard.

The god went round with calm and quiet steps to every patient looking at every disease. He sat down by Plutus. With a cloth of clean linen he wiped Plutus' eyelids a number of times. Next Panacea (the god's daughter) covered Plutus' head with a scarlet cloth. The god whistled and two huge serpents appeared. They crept under the scarlet cloth and licked his eyelids. Then Plutus sat up and he could see again, but the god, his helpers and the serpents had vanished.

From *Plutus*, a play by the Greek writer Aristophanes, c.400 BC

❖ *Can a play tell us anything about real-life methods used at the Asklepia?*

SOURCE 2

Carvings of Asklepios and his daughter Hygeia c. AD 400.

SOURCE 3

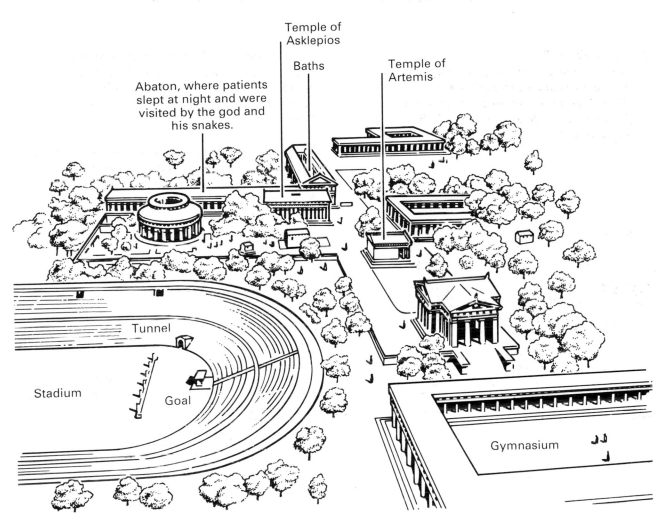

Temple of
Asklepios

Baths

Temple of
Artemis

Abaton, where patients
slept at night and were
visited by the god and
his snakes.

Tunnel

Stadium

Goal

Gymnasium

Reconstruction of the Asklepion at Epidaurus
as it was about 400 BC.

SOURCE 4 – A hospital in Cairo founded in 1276

It was endowed with an income of £25 000, and
contained four great courts each with a fountain in the
centre, wards for each separate disease, a lecture room,
and a department for attending patients in their own
homes. The convalescent patient received at his departure
about £2.50, that he might not be obliged to return to
work immediately.

British Medical Journal, 1908

SOURCE 5 – No alcohol or pork

Ritual cleanliness requires Muslims to wash themselves
regularly. The use of the toothbrush goes back to the Holy
Prophet. The same is true of dietary habits which include
not only total abstention from alcoholic drink and pork,
but also fasting, eating less than one's full appetite, and
eating slowly.

S. Hussein Nasr, *Islamic Science*, 1976

SOURCE 6

Abdallah ibn Buhktishu, a Persian doctor who helped to develop an
important hospital and medical training centre at Baghdad in the
8th century AD. Most towns in the Islamic world soon had a hospital
usually paid for out of religious funds. They gave free treatment to
the poor who needed it. From a 10th-century Arabic treatise on the
medicinal properties of plants and animals.

SOURCE 1

Carving c. AD 1000 from Constantinople showing the miracle of Christ healing the paralysed man, who is carrying away his bed.

SOURCE 2 – A miracle

A woman who had a continual bleeding for twelve years had suffered many things from many physicians. She had spent all that she had but was worse, not better. When she heard of Jesus she came in the crowd behind him and touched his clothes.

Straightaway the flow of blood was dried up, and she felt in her body that she was healed.

Jesus immediately turned around in the crowd and said, 'Who touched my clothes?'

The woman, fearing and trembling came and fell down before him, and told him all the truth. And he said to her, 'Daughter, your faith has cured you. Go in peace and be cured of your trouble.'

(Mark, chapter 5, New Testament. Written about AD 60 about events c. AD 30, Palestine.)

❖ *Would beliefs like this encourage or discourage the study of medicine?*

SOURCE 3 – Cure for toothache

Write these words on the jaw of the patient. 'In the name of the Father, Son and Holy Ghost, Amen. + Res + Pax + Nax + In Christo Filio.' The pain will cease at once as I have often seen.

John of Gaddesden, leading English doctor, c.1280–1361.

SOURCE 4

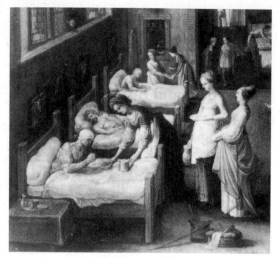

St Elizabeth of Hungary, 13th century. She devoted her life to helping the poor and the sick. She died at the age of 24. Oil painting by Adam Elsheiner, German, c. 1598.

SOURCE 5 – Sorcerers in every village

Sorcerers are common: cunning men, wizards, white witches as they call them, in every village. They will help almost any infirmity of body and mind. We see commonly the toothache, gout, falling sickness, biting of a mad dog, and many such maladies, cured by spells, words and charms.

R. Burton, *Anatomy of Melancholy*, 1621. At this time the Church attacked 'sorcerers' of this type, and some were put to death as witches.

❖ *What effects might attacks like this have on change and development in medicine.*

SOURCE 6

The Rock of the Apparition at Lourdes, where Bernadette Soubirous had a vision of the Virgin Mary in 1858. The vision is said to have repeatedly appeared to Bernadette and told her 'to drink at the spring and wash in it', which pilgrims still do. Many cures have been reported.

SOURCE 7

Scenes in a hospital, from a 14th-century French painting. Many hospitals were founded by the Church in Europe in the later Middle Ages.

SOURCE 8

King Charles II touching for the 'King's Evil' – scrofula. Engraving by R. White, 1684. The last English monarch to touch people to cure the 'King's Evil' was Queen Anne (1702-1714). After that, as the cartoon (right) implies, nobody took the idea seriously.

❖ *How can this change be explained? (clue – see page 38)*

SOURCE 9– Bangkok, Thailand, a three-year-old faith healer

Police used roadblocks at the weekend to stop a three-year-old faith healer using 'magic' tree bark to draw thousands of peasants to his village.

Aided by lavish media attention he drew crowds of believers to pay 20 baht (50p) for a bowl with candles, incense and the bark. Some came in chartered buses from as far away as Bangkok, 240 kilometres to the south-west.

His parents, interviewed in the Ban Muang daily, said that the boy could heal because a divine doctor had possessed him. Belief in spirits is widely prevalent in Thailand. A senior ministry official warned the public that their illness might worsen if they chose supernatural over proper treatment.

Guardian, 11 August 1986

2 WAR AND MEDICINE

KEY QUESTIONS

◆ *What medical improvements have wars encouraged?*

◆ *Why should wars encourage people to spend time and money on medical improvements?*

◆ *Were these improvements caused also by other factors, so that they would probably have happened in any case?*

◆ *What examples are there of wars hindering medical change or slowing it down?*

◆ *What important medical developments were little affected by war?*

Wars have caused death and destruction at every period of human history. There is no doubt about their harmful effect on people living at the time. But wars have also had an important effect on the way things change in history. Sometimes they have speeded up changes, or started new ones, and sometimes they have caused so much destruction that they have hindered new developments or stopped them altogether.

The timechart shows some wars which have been important in the history of medicine. The next two pages describe how wars have been an important factors in medical change. The case study on pages 84-85 describes the work of Ambroise Paré, a 16th-century French army surgeon, in more detail.

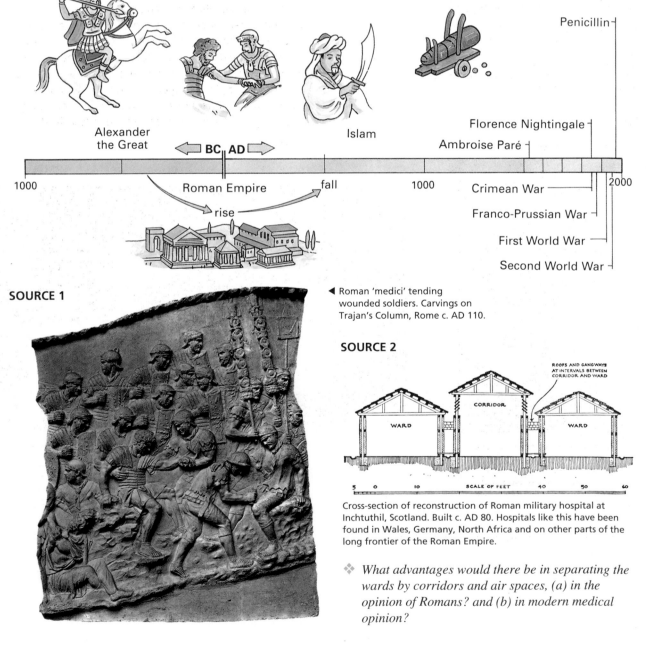

Penicillin

Florence Nightingale

Ambroise Paré

Alexander the Great

⬅ **BC** ‖ **AD** ➡

Islam

1000   Roman Empire   fall   1000   2000

rise

Crimean War

Franco-Prussian War

First World War

Second World War

SOURCE 1

◀ Roman 'medici' tending wounded soldiers. Carvings on Trajan's Column, Rome c. AD 110.

SOURCE 2

ROOFS AND GANGWAYS AT INTERVALS BETWEEN CORRIDOR AND WARD

CORRIDOR

WARD   WARD

5   0   10   SCALE OF FEET   40   50   60

Cross-section of reconstruction of Roman military hospital at Inchtuthil, Scotland. Built c. AD 80. Hospitals like this have been found in Wales, Germany, North Africa and on other parts of the long frontier of the Roman Empire.

❖ *What advantages would there be in separating the wards by corridors and air spaces, (a) in the opinion of Romans? and (b) in modern medical opinion?*

SOURCE 3

The Chinese surgeon Hua T'o cleaning an arrow wound in the arm of General Kuan Yu. Kuan Yu lived in the 3rd century AD. 'While the knife went "hsi hsi" scraping the bone, the general played a game and drank cups of wine.' From a Japanese colour woodcut, 19th century.

SOURCE 4

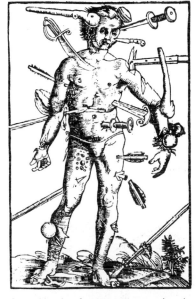

Several books of surgery were produced in the later Middle Ages. They often included a picture of a 'wound man' This one is from a book published in 1536, showing the kinds of wounds a surgeon could treat

❖ *What use would illustrations like this be to a surgeon?*

SOURCE 5 – New instruments every day

The methods employed for extracting arrows cannot be described in detail for every day we see new instruments and new methods being invented by clever and ingenious surgeons.

Theodoric of Lucca, *Surgery,* 13th century

War and Vaccination   In the Franco-Prussian War of 1870 the Prussian (German) army had a good system of vaccination: 297 of their men caught smallpox. The French army had no effective system of vaccination: 23 400 of their men caught smallpox.

❖ *What would be the likely effect of these figures?*

SOURCE 6 – The 1914–18 War encourages medical change

High velocity bullets and shrapnel produced severe wounds. X-rays of bones became commonplace. Bone surgery developed as a highly skilled branch of surgery. Despite steel helmets, 10 per cent of all injuries were to the head. Surgery of the eye, face, ear, nose and throat, and brain, and plastic surgery developed rapidly under war stimulus. Many surgeons who gained the necessary knowledge and experience later set up as 'specialists'.

C. Spry, *Medicine at War*, 1970

SOURCE 7

First World War. Attending wounded soldiers at the battle front, France 1915.

CASE STUDY   War and medical change: Ambroise Paré

Ambroise Paré was a French surgeon born in 1510. He was probably apprenticed to his brother, and, like most other surgeons, learned on the job rather than from books. At the age of 26 he became an army surgeon and spent the next twenty years on various campaigns.

Guns were increasingly used in the wars of the 16th century. They set a new problem for the surgeons – a bullet might carry infection deep into the wound. Once the infection caught hold, an arm or leg often had to be amputated. Amputation in turn often led to death through loss of blood.

The accepted method of dealing with these problems was to pour hot oil into gunshot wounds, and to seal the blood vessels of an amputation wound by searing with a red hot iron or 'cautery', as you can see in Source 1.

In Sources 2 and 5, Paré explains how he dealt with these problems.

SOURCE 1

Using a cautery iron. From *A manual of field surgery*, 1593.

SOURCE 2 – Paré runs out of oil

In the year 1536 the great King Francis sent an army to Turin.

. . . In the Chateau de Villaine there were about two hundred Spaniards. They killed and wounded a great number of our soldiers with pikes, arquebuses (guns) and stones. At that time I had not seen wounds made by gunshot. It is true that I had read in Jean de Vigo *Of Wounds in General*, chapter eight, that wounds made by firearms are poisonous because of the powder. For their cure he orders them to be cauterised with oil of elder, scalding hot. In order not to make any mistakes I wanted to know before using the oil what the other surgeons did for the first dressing. It was to apply the oil, as hot as possible, into the wound.

After a time I ran out of oil, and I had to apply instead a digestive made of yolks of egg, oil of roses and turpentine. That night I could not sleep at my ease, fearing that because I had not cauterised them I should find the wounded dead or poisoned. This made me get up very early to visit them.

Beyond my hope I found those on whom I had put the digestive medicament feeling little pain, and their wounds without inflamation having rested fairly well throughout the night. The others to whom I had applied the boiling oil, I found feverish, with great pain and swelling about their wounds. Then I resolved with myself never more to burn thus cruelly poor men wounded with gunshot.

Ambroise Paré, *The Apology and Treatise*, 1585

SOURCE 3

Contemporary painting of Paré in middle age.

SOURCE 4

Paré operating on a soldier. Photograph of modern museum reconstruction.

SOURCE 5 – How to stop the bleeding

When you have cut off the limb, let it bleed a little so that the rest of the part may afterwards be less likely to become inflamed. Then let the veins and arteries be tied up as speedily as you can so that the flowing of the blood may be stopped.

I confess that I used to staunch the bleeding after amputation in a different way, of which I am now ashamed. But what else could I do? I had watched my masters whose methods I intended to follow. They had various hot irons and burning medicines with which they would treat the dismembered part. This cannot be spoken of without great horror, for this kind of remedy could not help giving the patient great tormenting pain.

I must earnestly beg all surgeons to give up this old and too cruel way of healing, and take up this new method. I think that it was taught to me by the special favour of God, because I did not learn it from my masters.

Ambroise Paré, *Works on Surgery,* 1575, and *The Apology and Treatise,* 1585.

Paré's idea of tying the arteries was not completely new, but his books made it widely known. The Paris College of Physicians tried to prevent him publishing his ideas, but failed because the king supported him. The physicians opposed Paré because the old method of cauterising with a hot iron had been used for a very long time and they distrusted new ideas. But Paré's 'ligature' method, in which the surgeon tied off the arteries with a silk thread, did mean, before the days of antiseptics, that the wound was more likely to go septic and kill the soldier. It was not until the development of antiseptics by Lister 400 years later that Paré's method could be fully used.

After serving with the army, Paré became a very successful surgeon in Paris and was surgeon to three French kings in turn. In 1575 he published his *Works on Surgery.* This book was written in French, not Latin, but was translated into many languages and was widely read. Paré died in 1590 after a long and successful career.

❖ *Might Paré's methods have been developed and spread in much the same way even without his experience in war?*
❖ *Were the methods developed by Paré in war likely to be useful in peacetime medicine?*
❖ *How important was chance in leading Paré to his discoveries?*

3 GOVERNMENT AND MEDICINE

KEY QUESTIONS

◆ *When was government action important and when was it not very important?*

◆ *How can these differences be explained?*

◆ *Why did people sometimes oppose government action on health?*

◆ *What changes in medicine have been influenced very little by governments?*

◆ *What changes have been influenced a great deal?*

◆ *How important has government action been as a factor in the history of medicine?*

Governments have often been an important factor in the history of medicine. Sometimes a king or a Parliament has passed laws about medicine for a whole country. Sometimes the regulations made by a town council have caused important changes, or stopped them happening. Often some people have opposed changes that others wanted, so there have been political arguments about medicine.

Some factors like religion and wars, have been important throughout the history of medicine. Government is an example of a factor that was important at some times and of little importance at others. This is partly because the dangers to public health were not so serious at some times and places as at others. In a village or a small town people can get water pure enough to drink from their own wells or from a river. But as towns get bigger sewage is likely to soak into the soil and pollute the water. Some of the early cities, like those of Mesopotamia, Egypt or China were built on great rivers that brought fresh water and carried away waste at the same time, so there was no problem. But ancient Rome stood on the banks of the river Tiber, quite a small river that often ran low in the hot, dry Mediterranean summers. As the population rose the problems became so serious that the government took action.

❖ *What other times and places have there been when the problems of public health became serious and forced governments to act?*

There are other reasons why government action has varied a great deal. Some governments have cared much more than others about the health of ordinary people. At some times and places new medical discoveries have brought in new public health methods like vaccination.

The timeline below shows some examples of governments being involved in public health. Sources 1 to 6 on page 87 describe different aspects of public health over 3000 years. Three case studies make up the rest of this section. The first deals with government efforts to deal with the plague. The second looks at public health problems in British cities in the 19th century and the arguments for and against government action. The third case study looks at the arguments in Britain in the 20th century over how far the government should provide a free health service for everyone.

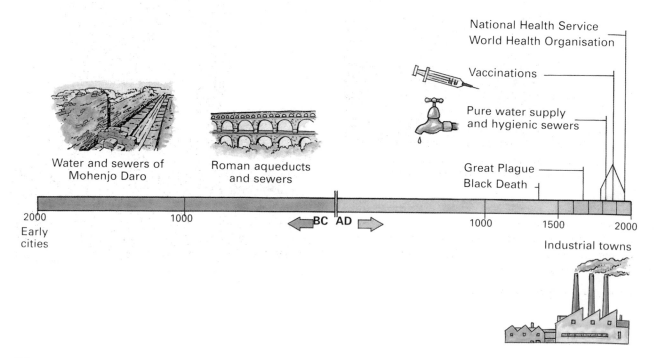

Water and sewers of Mohenjo Daro

Roman aqueducts and sewers

National Health Service
World Health Organisation

Vaccinations

Pure water supply and hygienic sewers

Great Plague
Black Death

2000
Early cities

1000

◁ BC AD ▷

1000

1500

2000

Industrial towns

The sources on this page cover over 3500 years.

❖ *Has public health care kept getting steadily better during this time?*

SOURCE 1

The Queen's bathroom at Knossos, Crete. Artist's reconstruction as it was c.1500 BC. Archaeologists have found an extensive system of water supply and drainage. The Minoan civilisation which built it was destroyed by an earthquake c.1400 BC.

SOURCE 2

Stone lavatory seats at the public latrine at Mokaio, Tunisia, the Roman city of Dougga, built 2nd to 4th century AD. Note the washbasin on the left.

SOURCE 3   Two tonnes of filth

For emptying two tonnes out of a privy in Harry Williamson's house – 5s 4d (27p).

Accounts of churchwardens, St Mary's, London, 1478

SOURCE 4

Water seller with ass carrying water bags from the Luttrell Psalter, c.1338.

SOURCE 5 – Human filth on people's heads

The jury decided that the lane called Ebbegate, which runs between the property of John de Pultenye and Thomas at Wytte used to be a right of way for all men until it was closed up by Thomas at Wytte and William de Hockele. They together built latrines which projected from the walls of the houses. From these latrines, human filth falls on the heads of the passers-by.

London Court Record, 1321

SOURCE 6

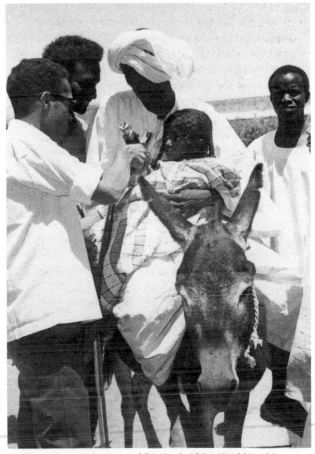

Health worker vaccinating a child. North Africa. World Health Organisation, 1976.

CASE STUDY 1 BUBONIC PLAGUE IN EUROPE

The 'Black Death' arrived in Europe in 1347. People who caught it came out in swellings that turned to boils and black spots, and after a few days most patients died. Whole villages were wiped out. The plague killed about a quarter of the population of Europe in the next few years. It then came back again and again until the 18th century.

It was only quite recently, in 1898–1914, that scientists worked out how bubonic plague is caused. The germ affects rats as well as humans, and when the rats die the fleas that suck their blood move on to the nearest humans and bite them instead, so spreading the germ. Wherever fleas, rats and people live close together, the disease can spread easily.

Use the sources on these pages to answer the following questions:

❖ *What did people think caused plague?*
❖ *How did they try to prevent plague spreading?*
❖ *Were any of the government's methods likely to work?*
❖ *Were any of their methods likely to make things worse?*
❖ *The last epidemic of plague in western Europe was in the 1720s. Does this mean that the methods they used must have been successful? What else might explain the ending of plague?*

SOURCE 1 – Filth lying in the streets

To the Lord Mayor of London

An order to cause the human excreta and other filth lying in the streets and lanes in the city and its suburbs to be removed with all speed. Also to cause the city and suburbs to be kept clean, as it used to be in the time of the previous mayors. This is so that no greater cause of death may arise from such smells. The king has learnt that the city and suburbs are so full with filth from out of the houses by day and night that the air is infected and the city poisoned. This is a danger to men, especially by the contagious sickness which increases daily.

Letter from King Edward III, 1349

SOURCE 2 – Avoid stinks

The pestilences come from three things. Sometimes from the ground below, at others from the atmosphere above and sometimes from both together as we see a privy next to a bedroom, or anything else that corrupt the air. Sometimes it comes from dead carrion or the corruption of stagnant waters in ditches.

Bishop Aarhus, *A Good Little Book against the Pestilence*, London, 1485.

SOURCE 3 – Orders by the Lord Mayor of London, 1665

Examiners
The examiners if they find any person sick of the Infection, to give order that the house be shut up.

Searchers
Women searchers to make search and true report whether the person die of the infection, or of what other diseases. No searcher to keep a shop or be employed as a laundress.

Shutting up of the sick
As soon as any man shall be found to be sick of the Plague, he shall the same night be shut up in the same house and the house shall be shut up for a month. None to be removed out of infected houses.

Burial of the dead
Burial to be always before sunrise or after sunset. All the graves shall be at least six feet deep.

House to be marked
Every house visited by the Plague to be marked with a red cross of a foot long, and with these words, 'Lord have mercy upon us'.

Houses to be watched
The constable to see every house shut up and attended with watchmen, who are to get food for the inhabitants at their own expense if they can afford it, at the public expense if they cannot.

Streets to be kept clean
Every household to keep the street clean before his door. No hogs, dogs, cats, pigeons or rabbits to be kept within any part of the city, or swine stray in the streets. Dogs to be killed by the dog-killers.

Published by the Lord Mayor, 1665. Over 60 000 people died in the Great Plague of London of that year.

SOURCE 4

Scene from a broadsheet published in 1666, the year after the Plague. It shows, among other things, women searchers and dog-killers.

SOURCE 5 – Some extracts from the Diary of Samuel Pepys, 1666

7 June I did in Drury Lane see two or three houses marked with a red cross upon the doors and 'Lord have mercy upon us' writ there - which was a sad sight. I was forced to buy some roll-tobacco to smell and chew.

12 August The people die so, that it now seems they carry the dead to be buried by daylight, the nights not sufficing to do it in.

20 September No boats upon the river; grass grows tall up and down Whitehall.

16 October So many poor sick people in the streets full of sores. In Westminster there is never a doctor and but one chemist left, all being dead.

SOURCE 6

The quarantine station at Naples in the 18th century, from J. Howard *An account of the Principal Lazarettos in Europe*, 1789. 'Quarantine' comes from an Italian word meaning '40 days'. People who might carry plague had to wait here for 40 days before being allowed into the city. This system was widely used in Europe in the 18th century.

QUESTIONS

1. Look at Source 1.
   (a) What does the king tell the Lord Mayor of London to do?
   (b) What ideas about the causes of disease is this based on?

2. Look at Source 3.
   The Lord Mayor's Orders of 1665 are much more detailed than the Order of 1349. Does that mean they must have been more effective?

3. Both these sources are official instructions. How useful are they to a historian in finding out what was actually done at the time?

4. Look at Source 4. How far does it support Source 3?

5. Read Source 5. How far does it support Source 3?

6. Look at Sources 3 and 5. What do these sources tell us about what people believed about the causes of the plague?

7. Was there any better understanding of the causes of the plague in 1665 than in 1349?

8. Look at Source 6. Do you think the Venetian government's rules about quarantine would be effective at preventing the plague from entering the city?

9. (a) Before the 20th century, all efforts to deal with the plague were useless.
   (b) Before the 20th century, governments did the best they could to prevent the plague from spreading.
   Use these sources and your own knowledge to say which of these statements you think is more accurate.

CASE STUDY 2   Government and public health in 19th-century Britain: the problem

SOURCE 1

A Court for King Cholera, 1840.

A new problem   In the 19th century Britain faced a new problem. Industrial towns like Leeds and Manchester grew like mushrooms. People moved into them far faster than houses or water supply or sewers could be built. They crowded into old houses or into hastily and shoddily built new ones as near to the factories as they could get. Smoke polluted the air, and refuse and industrial waste made the rivers foul and smelly.

Infectious diseases of all kinds were common. Coughing quickly spread tuberculosis and other diseases. People found it hard to keep clean, so many of them had body-lice and these spread typhus fever. Typhoid, diarrhoea, and other infections were common. As well as these well-known diseases, a new and deadly epidemic hit Britain in the 19th century – cholera. It was more frightening than the other diseases because it was new and it struck fast. It could kill healthy people in a few days. In 1831–32 it killed over 21 000 people in Britain and in 1849–50 over 50 000. Cholera killed fewer people over the years than the other infectious diseases like tuberculosis, but it frightened people far more.

Look at Sources 1 to 6.

❖ *How did conditions in the towns cause disease or encourage it to spread?*
❖ *How did cholera help doctors to prove the need for clean drinking water?*

SOURCE 2 – Filth of the most harmful character

The river Irk, black with the refuse of dye-works erected on its banks, receives excrement from some sewers in this portion of the town, the drainage of the gas-works and filth of the most harmful character from bone-works, tanneries etc. The parish burial ground occupies one side of the stream and a series of courts [yards with many dwelling houses] of the most unhealthy character the other.

Dr J. P. Kay, *The Moral and Physical Conditions of the Working Class in Manchester*, 1832

SOURCE 3 – 386 people to two lavatories

The Board will at once see how the disease (cholera) has been rampant in those parts of the town where there is often an entire lack of sewerage, drainage and paving. In one division of the town occupied entirely by cottage dwellings, including cellar dwellings, for 386 persons there are but two single privies. In such streets as these the Board will see the highest rate of cholera attacks.

Dr Robert Baker, *Report to the Leeds Boards of Health*, 1833

SOURCE 4

Dr Snow's map. The Broad Street pump is in the middle. Cases of cholera are marked. Which other pump may also have been infected?

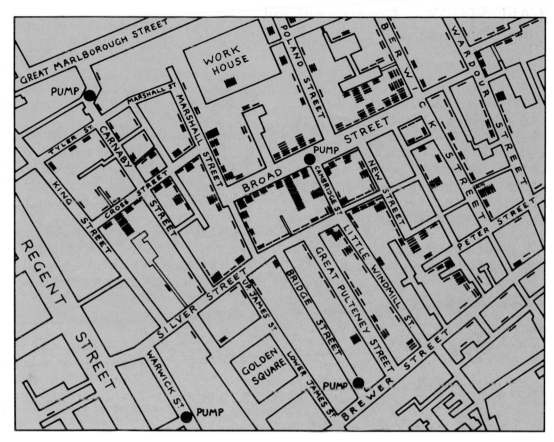

SOURCE 5 – The Broad Street pump

The most terrible outbreak of cholera is probably that which took place in Broad Street, Golden Square, London, and the adjoining street a few weeks ago. There were upwards of 500 fatal attacks in ten days.

See Snow's map. He marked where the victims lived.

There is a brewery in Broad Street, near to the pump, and on perceiving that none of the brewer's men were registered as having died of cholera, I called on Mr Huggins, the proprietor. He informed me that there were about seventy workmen employed in the brewery and that none of them had suffered from cholera, at least in a severe form. The men are allowed a certain quantity of beer, and Mr Huggins believes that they do not drink water at all. He is quite certain that workmen never obtained water from the pump in the street.

I had an interview with the Board of Guardians of St James parish on the evening of Thursday 7th September. In consequence of what I said the handle of the pump was removed on the following day.

Dr John Snow, *On the Mode of Communication of Cholera*, 1854. As soon as the people were no longer able to drink the pump water the epidemic stopped spreading in that area. Dr Snow concluded from this that cholera was carried by something in the water.

SOURCE 6

Drawing of a girl dying of cholera, Sunderland, c.1831.

In 1830 most people in Britain thought that looking after public health was not part of the government's duty. By 1875 they had changed their minds and agreed that it was. The cholera epidemics were one reason for the change. The information on pages 92 and 93 shows some of the others.

CASE STUDY 2   Government and public health in 19th-century Britain: opinion changes

KEY QUESTIONS

◆ *What were the arguments in favour of government action in public health?*
◆ *What were the arguments against?*
◆ *What factors helped to settle the argument?*
◆ *At the same time new discoveries were being made by Pasteur, Koch and others. Which was more important for health, these discoveries or the actions of governments?*

During the 19th century ideas about public health changed. Governments and people accepted that improving public health was part of the government's job.

Look at pages 92 to 95.

SOURCE 1

Edwin Chadwick

Edwin Chadwick was Secretary of the Poor Law Commission set up in 1834. He soon became convinced that one main cause of poverty was sickness. He thought that a good water supply and a clean sewage system was the best way to prevent this. He organised research by a group of doctors, and in 1842 he produced his *Report on the Sanitary Conditions of the Working Population* (see page 94, Source 1). In this he said that the central government in London should organise a proper public health system all over the country. In 1848, when Parliament set up a General Board of Health in London, Chadwick became its leading member. He tried to force local boards and town councils to make improvements. This made him very unpopular. People strongly disliked being ordered about by a civil servant like Chadwick. In 1854 his enemies persuaded the Government to sack him and to abolish the General Board of Health.

Who controlled the Government?

Until 1832   Parliament was controlled mainly by wealthy landowners. Many growing towns like Manchester had no MPs and no town council. Where a town had a council, councillors were appointed through influence and not elected by the people.

By the 1832 Reform Act   Most of the new industrial towns gained MPs, elected by a vote of the middle classes only.

In 1835   An Act of Parliament set up Town Councils in all the main towns. These were to be elected by all ratepayers, but many poor people did not pay rates and so could not vote. The main task of the new town councils was to keep law and order. They could do other things, like building sewers, if they wanted to, but the cost had to come out of the rates.

In 1867   Parliament was reformed again. The vote in towns was given to all male householders. This applied to elections for Parliament and for the town councils. So after 1867 most MPs and town councillors needed to gain the support of working-class voters.

SOURCE 2

William Farr

William Farr was a doctor who worked for the Registrar General of Births, Marriages and Deaths from 1839 to 1879. During the 1840s he brought in a system of accurate recording of the causes of all deaths in each district. A death certificate had to be signed by a qualified doctor, giving the cause. This meant that by the 1850s there were plenty of accurate statistics that could be used to show that disease was far worse where sewage and water systems were bad.

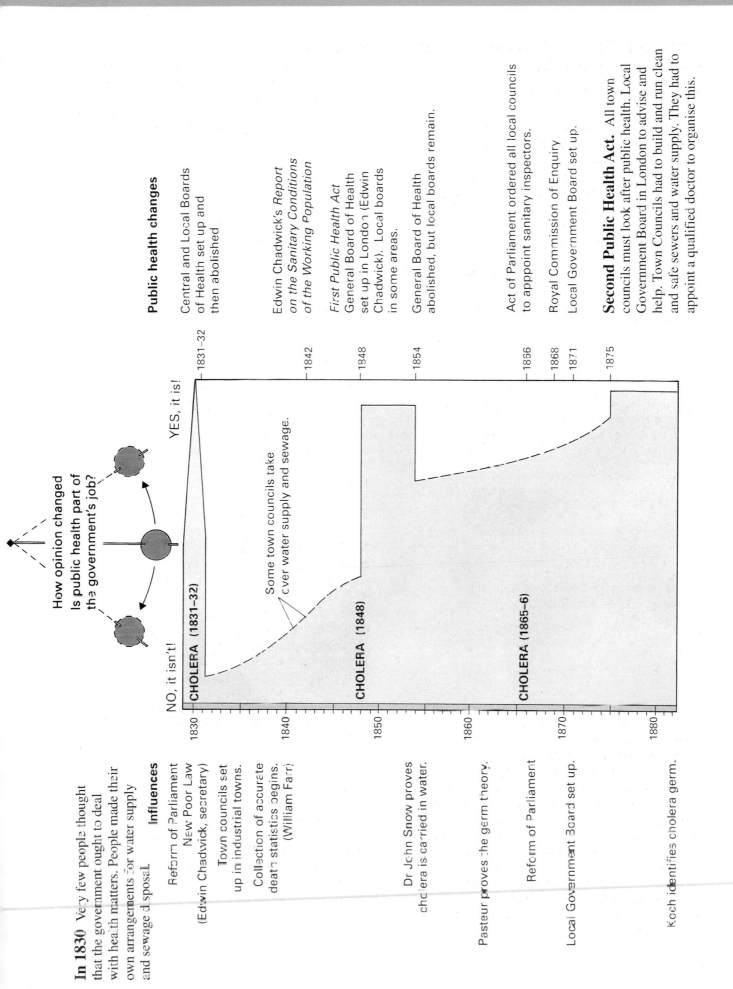

In 1830 Very few people thought that the government ought to deal with health matters. People made their own arrangements for water supply and sewage disposal.

Influences

Reform of Parliament
New Poor Law (Edwin Chadwick, secretary)

Town councils set up in industrial towns.

Collection of accurate death statistics begins. (William Farr)

Dr John Snow proves cholera is carried in water.

Pasteur proves the germ theory.

Reform of Parliament

Local Government Board set up.

Koch identifies cholera germ.

How opinion changed
Is public health part of the government's job?

YES, it is!

NO, it isn't!

CHOLERA (1831–32)

Some town councils take over water supply and sewage.

CHOLERA (1848)

CHOLERA (1865–6)

1830
1840
1850
1860
1870
1880

Public health changes

1831–32 Central and Local Boards of Health set up and then abolished

1842 Edwin Chadwick's *Report on the Sanitary Conditions of the Working Population*

1848 *First Public Health Act*
General Board of Health set up in London (Edwin Chadwick). Local boards in some areas.

1854 General Board of Health abolished, but local boards remain.

1856 Act of Parliament ordered all local councils to appoint sanitary inspectors.

1868 Royal Commission of Enquiry

1871 Local Government Board set up.

1875 **Second Public Health Act.** All town councils must look after public health. Local Government Board in London to advise and help. Town Councils had to build and run clean and safe sewers and water supply. They had to appoint a qualified doctor to organise this.

CASE STUDY 2 Government and public health in 19th-century Britain: for and against

For

In 1838 Dr Southwood Smith, who worked for Chadwick, investigated the crowded slums of Whitechapel in the East End of London. There were 27 000 paupers or poor people unable to support themselves. 14 000 of these, in his opinion, were poor because of 'fever', mostly because the breadwinner had died of it.

SOURCE 1 – Drains and pure water would save more money than they cost

After an examination of the evidence I conclude.

First: That the various forms of epidemic disease amongst the labouring classes are caused by atmospheric impurities produced by decaying animal and vegetable substances, by damp and filth, and close and overcrowded dwellings.

The annual loss of life from filth and bad ventilation are greater than the loss from death or wounds in any war in which the country has been engaged in modern times.

Second: That the most important measures and the most practical are drainage, the removal of all refuse from the streets and roads and the improvement of supplies of water.

The expense of public drainage and supplies of water would save money by cutting the existing charge resulting from sickness and mortality.

For the prevention of disease it would be a good economy to appoint a district medical officer with special qualifications.

Edwin Chadwick, *Report on the Sanitary Conditions of the Labouring Population*, 1842

Against

SOURCE 2 – Saving the pockets of the ratepayers

A proposal was made for the complete sewerage of the streets, carrying the main sewer clear of the river to a distance from the town. I was present for nearly six hours listening to the debate on this important subject. The chief theme of the speakers in opposition to the plan related to the means of saving the pockets of the ratepayers with very little regard to the sanitary results. A motion was carried to consider a plan of their own surveyor. This plan was more calculated to save money than to ensure efficiency. The main sewers by this plan were to discharge into the river at several points, thereby continuing the pollution. A careful economy in public money is most necessary, but health is now proved to be the means of production of wealth. To adopt inferior plans is a false economy.

James Smith, *Report on the Condition of the Town of Leeds*, 1844

❖ *What do you think was James Smith's own opinion?*

SOURCE 3 – There is nothing a man so much hates as being cleaned against his will

The Board of Health has fallen. We prefer to take our chance of cholera than be bullied into health. Everywhere the Board's inspectors were bullying, insulting and expensive. They entered houses and factories insisting on changes revolting to the habits or pride of the masters and occupants. There is nothing a man hates so much as being cleaned against his will, or having his floors swept, his walls whitewashed, his pet dung heaps cleared away, all at the command of a sort of sanitary bumbailiff. Mr Chadwick set to work everywhere, washing and splashing, and Master John Bull was scrubbed and rubbed till the tears came to his eyes and his fists clenched themselves with worry and pain.

The Times, 1 August 1854

SOURCE 4

'Lord Morpeth throwing Pearls before . . . Aldermen.' A cartoon from *Punch* magazine in 1848 commenting on the reaction of many town councils to the idea of a Public Health Act. Lord Morpeth was the Government Minister in charge of the 1848 Public Health Bill.

CASE STUDY 2 Government and public health in 19th-century Britain: government action

In each case the date given here is when a national system was begun. Most of these things were done locally in some places at earlier dates.

Factory Acts
1802+

Workhouses
– some medical care
but not much
1834

Accurate records of
causes of death, etc
1839

Isolation hospitals for
infectious diseases
1899

Compulsory vaccinations
1852

Government and
local councils

Regulation of doctors'
qualifications
1858

Dr. J. Spog
M.R.C.P.
F.R.C.S.

Building regulations
1876

Laws against pollution
of rivers
1876

Clean water
1875

Hygienic sewers
1875

CASE STUDY 3 Government and public health in 20th-century Britain: poverty and disease

People have always known that good health depends as much on being able to afford proper food and clothing and decent housing as it does on clean drinking water or sewers. By 1900 it was clear that government and local councils were solving the problems of water and sewers. But there were millions of people who could not afford even to give their children proper food, much less to pay doctors' bills. Some people began to suggest that the best way for the government to improve the health of the nation was to tackle this problem.

The sources on pages 96 and 97 show the problems about the year 1900. On pages 98 and 99 are some of the arguments for and against government action.

❖ *What evidence is there in Sources 1 to 6 that the poor needed more help from the government?*

❖ *Which piece of evidence would be likely to influence a government most?*

SOURCE 1

Well-fed, middle-class children of about 1900.

SOURCE 2

Working-class children of about 1900, queuing for free food parcels.

SOURCE 3 – Over a quarter in poverty

In this land of unbounded wealth, during a time of perhaps unexampled prosperity, probably more than a quarter of the population are living in poverty. This is a fact that may well cause great searching of heart.

B.S. Rowntree, *Poverty, A Study of Town Life*, 1901. Rowntree's report was based on a careful study of poverty in York in 1899. He found that at any one time one family in ten earned so little that they could not possibly make ends meet even if they never wasted a penny and never had a day off work.

SOURCE 4 – Height and weight of 13-year-old children, Manchester 1913

	Height (cm)	Weight (kg)
Girls		
Poor class schools	137	34
Medium class schools	137	35
Good class schools	145	38
Boys		
Poor class schools	132	32
Medium class schools	137	33
Good class schools	145	37

The Lancet, 17 January 1914

SOURCE 5

British soldiers during the Boer War. 40 per cent of the men who volunteered from some towns were found to be medically unfit.

SOURCE 6

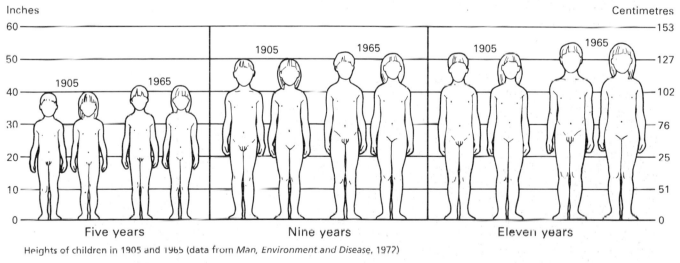

Heights of children in 1905 and 1965 (data from *Man, Environment and Disease,* 1972)

❖ *How much taller were the 11-year-olds in 1965 than in 1905?*

❖ *Does it seem likely from this that the differences between rich and poor had been reduced?*

CASE STUDY 3
Government and public health in 20th-century Britain: for and against a government health service

KEY QUESTIONS
◆ *Why did some people think that government action was needed?*
◆ *Why did others oppose this?*

Cartoon from the *Daily Mirror*, May 1946. It shows support for and objections to a National Health Service. The figure on the left is the Secretary of the British Medical Association, the main organisation of the doctors.

The sources on this page illustrate the arguments for and against government involvement.

For

SOURCE 1

SOURCE 2 – If only the State could do something

My experience during and after my second pregnancy is only one example of what thousands have to endure. I had to work at laundry work from morning to night, nurse a sick husband and take care of my child 3½ years old. I also had to do without food to provide doctor's fees for my coming confinement. When my baby was born I nearly lost my life – the doctor said through want of food. I had to depend on my neighbours for help. I was often left 6 hours without a bite of food, the fire out and no light. The time was January and the snow had lain on the ground for two weeks. When I got up after ten days my life was a perfect burden to me. I lost my milk and ultimately my baby.

Can we wonder why so many women take to drugs to get rid of the baby? If only the State could do something to give all working women help, so that during pregnancy they could get rest and proper attention! It would make all the difference – a safe and speedy confinement, a better offspring, and a better asset to the State.

Letter no 5, Maternity: *Letters from Working Women*, .ed. Margaret L. Davies, 1915

SOURCE 3 – Health is a National Concern

Modern methods of diagnosis and treatment are becoming so elaborate and costly that only the rich can afford to purchase these advantages. Many a patient has lost his life through trying to save a doctor's bill. Health is of national concern and disease is a national danger, hence the health of every individual, rich or poor, is of national importance, and its preservation should be undertaken by the nation collectively.

Beatrice Webb, *The Organisation of the Medical Services,* Labour Party pamphlet, 1918

SOURCE 4 – 'It is the mothers who get left out,' District Nurse

Most of the people pay into the hospital scheme 3d (1.25p) a week for the family. They also mostly pay into the nursing association scheme 1s 1d (5p) a quarter which covers my visits. Otherwise my visits cost 6d (2.5p) each. Children under 5 and expectant mothers in big families can get one pint of milk a day for each of them. Fathers and children at work come under the National Health Insurance. It is the mother who gets left out as far as treatment goes. She can go to hospital for teeth, but she cannot afford the transport or, as a rule, the time. She may get the 'family' doctor for herself and the children if she pays into the medical club. If she does not pay in she carries on as long as she can without advice or treatment. She will not start a doctor's bill for herself if she can possibly stand on her feet.

Margery Spring Rice, *Working-Class Wives,* 1939

SOURCE 5 – Aneurin Bevan explains his Bill

Medical treatment should be made available to rich and poor alike in accordance with medical need and no other criteria. Worry about money in a time of sickness is a serious hindrance to recovery, apart from its unnecessary cruelty. The records show that it is the mother in the average family who suffers most from the absence of a full health service. In trying to balance her budget she puts her own needs last. No society can call itself civilised if a sick person is denied medical aid because of lack of means. The essence of a satisfactory health service is that the rich and poor are treated alike, that poverty is not a disability and wealth is not advantaged.

Aneurin Bevan, Minister of Health, speech, 1946

SOURCE 6

From *Punch*, 1948. 'It all tastes awful.' Aneurin Bevan, Minister of Health is drawn as Mrs Squeers in *Nicholas Nickleby*, giving the doctors unpleasant medicine.

SOURCE 7

Daily Mirror, September 1945. (Vested interests – people who are doing well from the existing system.)

❖ *Many doctors opposed the new NHS. Are the cartoons sympathetic to Bevan, to the doctors or to neither?*

Against

SOURCE 8 – Wasting money on betting and drink

It is certain that some of the earnings which might go to buy necessaries are wilfully thrown away. Mr Rowntree refers to the prevalence of betting in York. The bookmaker probably absorbs as much of the working man's money as the publican. Public houses are not sufficient for the appetite of the people (in York), who have supplemented them by nine purely drinking clubs In addition to five political clubs where drink is sold. In one of these clubs the bill for intoxicants in 1899 was £1612. The word poverty in its ordinary sense is not properly applied to persons who might live in comfort if they did not squander money on betting and drink.

The Times, 21 December 1901, commenting on Rowntree's book.

SOURCE 9 – What will they ask for next?

We have already reduced personal responsibility by relieving parents of the duty of educating their children. This is now used as an argument for relieving them of the duty of feeding their children. When we have done that the argument will be stronger for relieving them of the duty of clothing their children. From that it is an easy step to paying for their proper housing. The proposed measure (free school meals for the poorest children) would go far to sap the remaining independence of the parents. The habit of looking to the State for maintenance would be ingrained.

The Times, 2 January 1905

SOURCE 10 – Getting something for nothing will harm people

I am unable to accept the proposal to set up a national medical service based upon the family doctor. The pernicious habit of getting something for nothing will be encouraged which is bound to have a detrimental effect on the morale of the people.

Sir Andrew Grierson, *Report of the Committee on a Scottish Health Service*, 1936

SOURCE 11 – No patient or doctor will feel safe

If the Bill is passed no patient or doctor will feel safe from interference by some ministerial edict or regulation. The Minister's spies will be everywhere, and intrigue will rule.

British Medical Journal, 18 January 1946

SOURCE 12 – Doctors would lose their freedom

The Bill threatens the independence of the general practitioner. The doctors have a justifiable dread of becoming government servants.

Daily Sketch, 5 February 1946

CASE STUDY 3 Government and public health in 20th-century Britain: the National Health Service

New political ideas – a demand for equality In the years 1900–1914 the contrast between rich and poor seemed to be increasing and many people felt that it was unfair. Some, the socialists, argued that the whole system of property ownership was unfair and should be changed. Together with the Trade Unions they formed a new political party, the Labour Party. The two older parties, the Liberals and the Conservatives, opposed socialism but they both agreed that more should be done to help the poor, especially to help their children to get a fair start. The Liberals were much keener on this than the Conservatives, and between 1906 and 1914 they brought in many useful social reforms, including a National Insurance system. All wage earners had to pay into this scheme by sticking stamps on an insurance card. In return they got sick pay and free medical care when they were ill, but this was only for the wage earners themselves, not for their dependants.

At this time many women were beginning to demand greater equality. They had no votes and they were kept out of the most important jobs. It was the educated women of the richer classes who led this movement for equality, but some of them could see that the women of the poorer classes were far worse off. Poor women had to bear the double inequality of being poor and being women.

The 1914–18 War increased these demands for equality. At the end of the war the ordinary soldiers who had fought in the trenches were the heroes, and the women who had worked in munitions factories or as nurses were the heroines. One result was that in 1918 all men and some women were given the vote. In 1928 the system was made the same for both sexes.

This change, and the growing sense of equality, did not lead to many new reforms in the 1920s and 1930s. The governments were mainly Conservative and they felt that the country could not afford to spend more money on health. Many of them argued that giving people medical care without making them pay for it would destroy their self-respect. But despite this, the reforms brought in by the Liberals before the war were continued and developed (see diagram on pages 64 and 65).

SOURCE 1

A poster issues by the Liberal Party in 1911, on David Lloyd George's National Insurance Scheme. The National Insurance Bill was passed as an Act of Parliament in 1911.

❖ *Why did the artist draw Lloyd George sitting at the bedside of a man, not a woman?*

SOURCE 2

A different view of Lloyd George as a wicked giant. The figure under the table is a rich man. (From *Punch*, 1909)

The Second World War and the coming of the National Health Service During the war enemy air-raids killed and injured rich and poor alike. Everybody from all classes had to work as part of the war effort, so good medical services for all were essential for victory. Medical care had to be provided whether people could pay for it or not. So the government organised an emergency system and by the end of the war most people in Britain were used to getting free medical services when they needed them. When the war ended all political parties agreed that a national health system was needed, but they disagreed about what it should be like.

In 1945 the Labour Party won the General Election with an overwhelming majority. They had promised the voters that if they won they would look after the welfare of all classes of people in housing, education, social care and health. In the years 1945–51 the Labour Government set up what came to be called the 'Welfare State'.

An important part of this was the National Health Service. The basic idea was to make all forms of health care freely available to everyone (see diagram, pages 64 and 65). The Minister of Health was Aneurin Bevan, the most outspoken socialist in the Government, and this worried the doctors and the Conservative Party. So in 1946 they strongly opposed the Health Service Bill.

Despite this opposition the Bill was passed and in 1948 the NHS came into existence. Nearly all doctors joined it. In 1951 it was changed slightly – charges were brought in for some services. On the whole, however, like the rest of the Welfare State it was accepted by the Conservative Government when it came into power in 1951.

After 1979 strong Conservative governments, led until 1990 by Margaret Thatcher, tried to cut the cost of the NHS and encouraged people to pay for private medical care. In 1990 they reorganised the National Health Service so that doctors were forced to think carefully about the cost of treatment as well as the patient's needs. This led to bitter disputes with doctors, nurses and the other political parties, but the Conservatives insisted that they were only trying to improve the NHS. People were used to having the National Health Service after 40 years, so the idea that the state should provide health care freely to all who needed it was popular and familiar.

SOURCE 3 – Death and disease rising with unemployment and poverty

Class-linked health gap wider

Death rates among young semi-skilled and unskilled workers aged 25–44 are more than twice as high as those for professional men of the same age.

Women have also suffered. Those married to men in social classes IV and V are up to 70 per cent more likely to die young than those in classes I and II.

The figures for 1979–83 come from the Government statistics service, the Office of Population Censuses and Surveys, in its report on occupational mortality.

Andrew Veitch, *Guardian*, 30 July 1986. Extract from a report that suggests that the NHS has not made health standards the same for everybody in Britain.

❖ *Why might differences still exist?*

❖ *What factors enabled Bevan and others to win the argument and set up the NHS?*

Wage earners got sick pay and medical care as part of National Insurance scheme

VOTES FOR WOMEN

Women campaigned to get the vote, which was gained in 1918.

Medical services were necessary during World War II. It was agreed that a National Insurance scheme was needed after the war

Aneurin Bevan, Minister of Health in the Labour government of 1945, organised the National Health Service, set up in 1948

4 SCIENCE, TECHNOLOGY AND MEDICINE

KEY QUESTIONS
◆ *How have science and technology brought changes in medicine?*
◆ *Why is scientific thinking important in medicine?*
◆ *Have there been times when science has been an important factor in medicine and times when it has not?*
◆ *Have there been times when new technology has been an important factor in medicine and times when it has not?*

1. Science and medicine

The development of medicine has been influenced very much by changes in knowledge of the human body and in theories about how it works. The time chart shows two periods of history when theories changed in important ways, and two of the ways in which new theories have led to new methods.

If you want to be a doctor you need good A level or higher grades in at least two of the main sciences studied at school: physics, chemistry and biology. This is partly because scientists have built up a body of knowledge that is essential to the work of a doctor – for instance knowledge about the blood vessels and the working of the heart, or about the cells of which the body is made up.

Another reason why doctors need to study science is that modern medicine is based on the 'scientific method'.

❖ *How does the way you study science differ from the way you study history or English?*

Early science and modern science

A special method of thinking and research was first developed in Europe in the 16th century. It led to the period labelled 'modern science' on the time chart. Since then scientists have used it to build up a detailed knowledge of the workings of the body. They can test and check each part of this knowledge so that it is difficult for anyone to disagree. Doctors need to understand this scientific method so that they can use its results intelligently and continue with new research.

The diagram on page 103 explains the main difference between the two sorts of scientific thinking. The change from one to the other did not happen all at once. Some parts of 'scientific method' had been used for a long time. Some were not fully understood until the 19th century. The sources on the next two pages will help you to follow the change.

❖ *What were the main differences between the two sorts of thinking?*

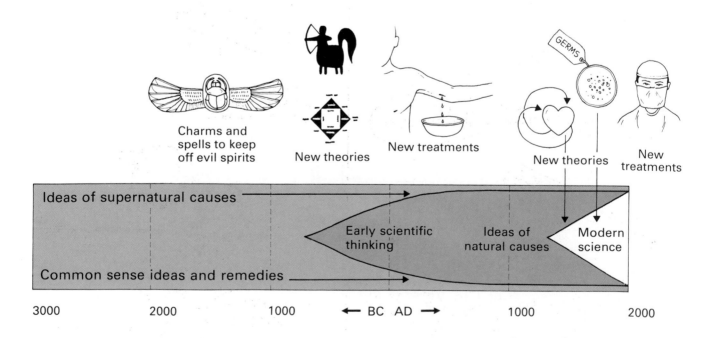

Charms and spells to keep off evil spirits

New theories

New treatments

New theories

New treatments

Ideas of supernatural causes

Early scientific thinking

Ideas of natural causes

Modern science

Common sense ideas and remedies

3000   2000   1000   ← BC AD →   1000   2000

The development of scientific thinking – some examples

❖ *In what ways do these sources show 'scientific method' being used or partly used, or not used at all?*

❖ *The sources cover a period of over 600 years. Why should it take so long for such a good idea as 'scientific method' to be fully accepted?*

SOURCE 1 – We should rely on research

There is no passage between the two cavities of the heart. It does not contain a visible passage, nor does it contain an invisible passage as Galen thought. It must therefore be that when the blood has become thin it is passed into the lung to mix with the air. The finest parts of the blood are then strained and pass into the left chambers of the heart. In determining the use of each organ we should rely on verified examination and straightforward research, disregarding whether our opinions agree or disagree with those of earlier writers.

Ibn an-Nafis, Cairo 1242, quoted in the *Dictionary of Scientific Biography*

SOURCE 2 – The causes of plague

Many people were in doubt about the causes of the great death. In some places it was believed that the Jews had poisoned the people. In others it was the poor cripples and in others it was the nobles.

But whatever the people said, the truth is that there were two causes, one general, one particular. The general cause was the close position of the three great planets Saturn, Jupiter and Mars. This had taken place in 1345 on the 24th March in the 14th degree of Aquarius. Such a coming together of planets is always a sign of wonderful, terrible or violent things to come.

The particular cause of the disease in each person was the state of the body – bad digestion, weakness and blockage, and for this reason the people died.

Guy de Chauliac, *Surgery*, 14th century

SOURCE 3 – Trying out a remedy

In Persia is a certain kind of goat in whose stomach the stone called Bezoar grows. It will dissolve in water.

Some years ago a certain gentleman who had one of these stones bragged before the King of the power of this stone against all poisons. The King asked me whether there was any antidote (remedy) which would work equally well against all poisons. I answered that all poisons do not work in the same way. Therefore each must be dealt with by its own antidote or opposite, like opposing something hot with something cold.

It was an easy matter to try it out on people condemned to be hanged. The King liked this suggestion, and a cook was brought, who was to have been hanged for stealing two silver dishes. The King first asked him if he would take some poison on this condition – if the antidote which would be given to him afterwards should work, then he should be allowed to live.

The cook answered cheerfully that he was willing to take the risk. The poison was given him and immediately after the poison some of the bezoar.

Soon after he began to vomit and to cry out that his inward parts were burnt with fire. When he asked for water they gave him some.

An hour later I found him on the ground like a beast on his hands and feet, with his tongue thrust out of his mouth, his eyes fiery, vomiting and with blood flowing out of his ears, nose and mouth. I gave him eight ounces of oil to drink, but it did him no good.

At length he died in great torment, in the seventh hour from the time he took the poison. I opened his body and I found the bottom of his stomach dry as if it had been burnt with a cautery.

Ambroise Paré, *Apology and Treatise*, 1585

Pasteur's experiment

In 1858–65 Pasteur was trying to prove that germs carried by the air cause the micro-organisms found in decaying organic matter. Other scientists argued that it went bad on its own – the micro-organisms were 'spontaneously generated'.

1. *Careful observation*
   Pasteur collected dust from the air, and found micro-organisms in it. He then found the same micro-organisms in decaying organic matter.

2. *Exact measurement*
   Everyone knew that heat killed micro-organisms. Pasteur measured exactly what temperature was needed. Some lived at up to 125°C.

3. *Clear thinking*
   Pasteur saw clearly the need to prove that it was the dust and not something else, like the air itself, that made things go bad. He designed an experiment to do this.

4. *Experiment*

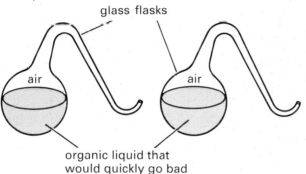

glass flasks

air air

organic liquid that would quickly go bad

   a. Pasteur heated the flasks, the liquid and the air to above 125°C. He was now certain that there were no live germs in the flasks.

THIS SHOULD BE AN INTERESTING EXPERIMENT, WHETHER HE LIVES OR DIES

b. All flasks were allowed to cool. As long as they were not shaken or tipped up, the liquid did not go bad.

c. The necks of some flasks were broken so allowing the air to carry dust into them.

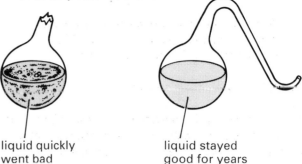

liquid quickly went bad

liquid stayed good for years

d. The experiment was repeated with many flasks under many different conditions. The results was always the same.

SOURCE 4 – Spontaneous generation proved wrong

The liquid in the second flask will remain pure for three or four years, for the experiment I am telling you about is already four years old. What difference is there between these two flasks? They contain the same liquid, they both contain air, both are open! Why does one decay and the other remain pure?

The only difference between them is this: in the first case the dust suspended in the air and its germs can fall into the neck of the flask and arrive in contact with the liquid, where they find appropriate food and develop. In the second flask on the contrary, it is impossible that dust suspended in the air should enter the flask; it falls on its curved neck. Only one thing cannot enter easily, and that is the dust suspended in the air. The proof of this is that if I shake the flask violently two or three times, in a few days it contains 'little animals' or mouldiness. Why? Because air has come in violently enough to carry dust with it. Never will the doctrine of spontaneous generation recover from the mortal blow of this simple experiment.

Louis Pasteur, Part of a lecture given at the University of Paris, 7 April 1864.

❖ *What made Pasteur's experiment so convincing?*

2. Technology and medicine

Technology is knowing how to make and do practical things like cooking the dinner or launching a space ship. Medicine is itself a technology, a practical way of treating sick people, and it has always depended very much on other technologies, such as the ability to make knives or to write books.

❖ *What other technologies did medicine depend on in prehistoric societies, or among nomadic hunter/gatherers in more recent times?*

❖ *What other technologies did medicine depend on in ancient or medieval times?*

SOURCE 1

Carving from an Egyptian tomb c.100 BC. It shows various surgical instruments.

SOURCE 3

Pharmacy, from a 15th-century European manuscript.

SOURCE 2

Dentist's drill drawn from an Islamic book, 9th century.

SOURCE 4

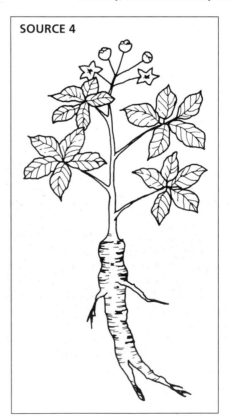

Ginseng, a medicinal herb, from a Chinese medical book, 1597.

CASE STUDY Technology and medicine: the microscope

In the last 200 years medicine has come to depend more and more on other technologies, such as that of preparing purified chemicals or making electrical machines. Many of these have themselves been made possible by scientific knowledge. For instance without the work of chemists like Sir Humphrey Davy, the chemicals used as anaesthetics could not have been prepared. So science has helped to make improvements in technology possible. But the connection has often been the other way round. Many scientific advances have been made possible by improvements in technology. One example of this is the microscope.

About the year 1600 European scientists and craftsmen produced a remarkable new instrument, the microscope. Craftsmen had been making lenses for spectacles since about 1300. In the 16th century improvements took place in glass-making and in the science of optics (the study of rays of light). One of the people who first made and used both telescopes and microscopes was the great Italian scientists Galileo (see Source 6).

Science was fashionable in 17th-century Europe, and people were fascinated by the new world of tiny creatures. Scientific workers began to study them and to try to understand them, but it was to be a long time before this had much effect on medicine.

Read the story of the development of microscopes on pages 107 to 109.

❖ *What scientific and technological developments helped to make microscopes useful for doctors?*

SOURCE 5

17th-century German print of spectacle-maker's shop. Spectacles had first been made in the 13th century.

SOURCE 6 – Infinite wonder and delight

Here is an instrument for examining minute things at a near distance. I hope that you will have as much use and joy in it as I have. With infinite wonder I have examined many minute creatures, amongst which the most horrible is the flea and the most beautiful the ant and the moth. With delight I have seen how flies and other little animals can walk on mirrors and even upside down.

Letter from Galileo to his friend, Cesi, Italy c.1610. Galileo was the first scientist to make and use a microscope, in 1610. He got the idea from a Dutch spectacle maker.

SOURCE 7

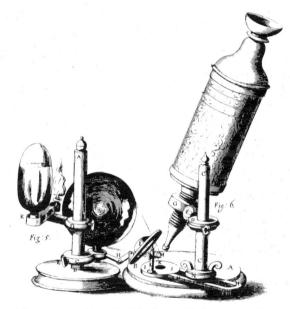

Microscope used by Robert Hooke, and (below, Source 8) Hooke's drawing of a flea. From Hooke's book *Micrographia*, 1665. Hooke worked for the Royal Society of London, founded in 1662 to encourage scientific knowledge.

SOURCE 8

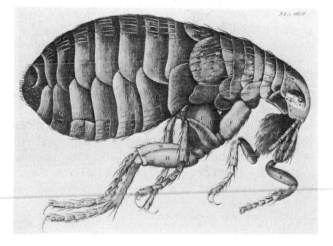

CASE STUDY   Technology and medicine: the microscope

The early microscopes had many problems. One man, Anton van Loewenhoek, was actually able to see and draw pictures of bacteria (Source 1), but nobody else had as much skill and perseverance, and many of the things he saw were not seen again until the 19th century. Most microscopes had two or more lenses, but this caused distortion. In 1671, Isaac Newton discovered a scientific explanation for this that seemed to make high-powered microscopes impossible.

The low-powered microscopes did make one important contribution to medicine, even in the 17th century. Marcello Malpighi was Professor of Medicine at Bologna in Italy. In 1661 he used his microscope to discover the capillary blood vessels. William Harvey had argued in 1628 that the blood circulating round the body must pass through tiny vessels of this sort, but they were too small for him to see. So the microscope established the truth of his basic theory. But its main importance for the next 150 years was in enabling scientists to learn more about living matter. A few people did suggest that the tiny organisms that could be seen through a microscope might cause sickness, but this did not seem very likely. How could such tiny things alter the balance of humours of the whole body?

Microscopes in the 19th century

By about 1800 the science of optics had solved some of the problems that Newton had seen. At the same time the glass-making industry had greatly improved and much purer glass than before could be made. It was Joseph Lister, father of the famous surgeon, who in 1830 solved the last problems of microscope design and made an instrument that could magnify up to about 1000 times with no distortion. At last scientists could examine micro-organisms really effectively.

What they saw seemed at first to show that existing theories were right. The tiny organisms that they could see in decaying matter or in the pus from a festering wound looked like proof of the widely held theory of spontaneous generation. It looked as if the microbes were developing out of the dead matter. The opposite theory was that the microbes could only be caused by other microbes multiplying. A few 17th-century scientists had suggested that this might be so, but there had been no way of proving or disproving it. Now there was. From 1830 until the 1880s the new microscopes were used on both sides of the argument, and finally helped to solve it conclusively. Pasteur used one to study the microbes that make beer and wine go bad. Koch used one to identify and photograph the microbes causing anthrax and other diseases. By about 1890 the germ theory of disease was well established and the microscope was being used in the search for ways of killing the germs.

SOURCE 1

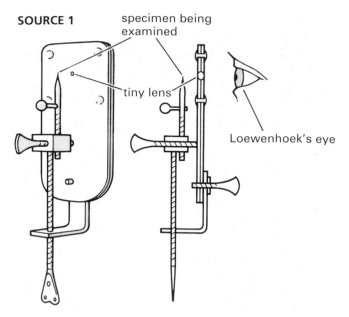

Anton van Loewenhoek's microscope. It had a single lens that he held very close to his eye. It could magnify about 275 times. It was made in Holland, c.1670.

SOURCE 2 – Living animals on my teeth

It is my habit every morning to clean my teeth, yet despite this a little white matter sticks between some of my front ones and my grinders. It is as thick as if it was batter. In this matter there were many little animalcules, very prettily a-moving. The biggest had the shape of figure A. These had a very strong, swift motion and shot through the spittle as a pike does through water. The second sort had the shape of figure B. These often spun round like a top.

Anton Van Loewenhoek, *The Secrets of Nature Discovered*, 1695

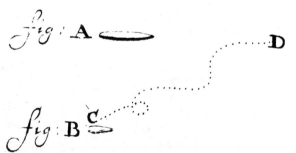

SOURCE 3

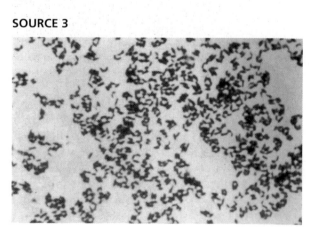

The microbes causing diphtheria magnified 1200 times. Microphotograph, 1986.

SOURCE 5

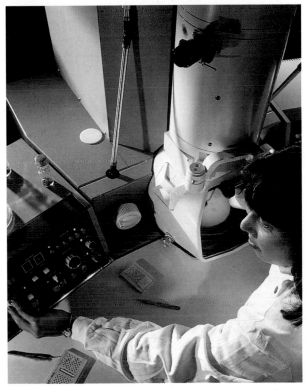

Electron microscope, 1994.

SOURCE 6

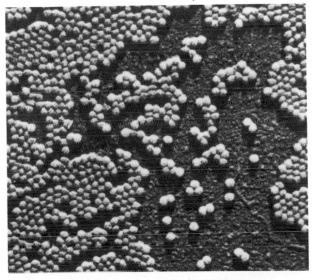

Polio virus (x 225,000). Photograph taken with an electron microscope, 1986.

Microscopes and medicine in the 20th century

The germ theory is only one example of the way the microscope has been used to explore the workings of the body and the causes of disease. Another is the detailed study of animals like mosquitoes or rats, which transmit disease organisms.

As well as its use in research, the microscope has also become essential to ordinary medical care. Specimens of many kinds are sent every day to hospital laboratories. Here microscopic examination is made, so that doctors can recognise a disease or see how a treatment is getting on.

As research continued in the 20th century a new problem arose. Some very important objects are too small to be seen at all with a microscope that uses ordinary light, because the light-waves are of a fixed size. The 'viruses', the organisms that cause some diseases such as polio or influenza, are smaller than this and so cannot be seen.

At the same time as this problem became clear, however, physicists were learning more about the electrons and other particles of which all matter is composed. Engineers and other technologists were also developing new electrical machines of many kinds. The result, in 1931, was the electron microscope, which uses electron beams instead of light. It was with an electron microscope that the American David Bodian identified the polio virus in 1949, and Jonas Salk made a vaccine against it in 1954. By the later 1950s an electron microscope could magnify up to a million times and it brought many new organisms and structures into view.

The development of the electron microscope is a good example of the way in which one technology depends on many others. Without the development of electrical machines it would have been impossible.

❖ *What other technical developments were necessary before electrical machines could be developed?*

Technical developments do not happen on their own without changes of other sorts happening at the same time.

❖ *What non-technical changes had to happen before electron microscopes or other electrical machines could be made, or hospitals staffed with skilled workers to use them?*

The microscope is just one example of how science technology and medicine have worked together. You will find many others on the next page.

Modern science, technology and medicine: some connections

Since about 1800, and increasingly since 1900, science, technology and medicine have developed at great speed. This diagram shows *some* of the ways in which they have influenced each other.

All these sciences have really worked together with each other, although they are shown separately.

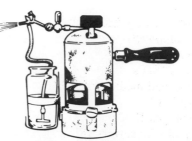

What science has done

Chemistry
- helped in understanding the chemistry of the body, e.g. in digestion
- made new materials (see opposite)
- purified old materials, e.g. drugs from herbs
- helped in understanding the working of the body

Biology
- helped in understanding the working of the body
- helped in understanding plants and animals, e.g. bacteria, germ theory 1861
- made new materials, e.g. antibiotics 1941+
- genetic engineering 1980s

Physics
- helped in understanding the working of the body, e.g. temperature, blood pressure, nerve currents
- electricity (see opposite)
- discovered radio activity and X-rays
- magnetism

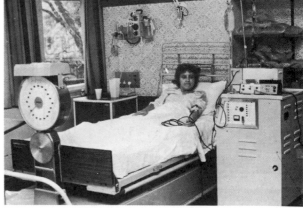

What technology has done

Made new materials
- anaesthetics 1840s
- antiseptics 1860s
- new drugs and medicines 1909+
- radium 1898
- radio-isotopes 1950s
- glazed pipes for sewers 1830s
- rubber 1890
- plastics 1940s
- stainless steel 1920s
- aluminium 1880s

Made machines to help in diagnosis
- microscope 1830+ } in practical
- thermometer 1852 } use
- manometer (to measure blood pressure) 1876
- stethoscope 1816
- **X-ray machine** 1896
- **electrocardiograph** (to measure electric currents in the heart) 1903
- **ultrasound body scanner** 1970+
- **magnetic resonance scanner** 1980+

Made machines to help in treatment
- **radiation machines** 1900s
- **incubators** (for premature babies)
- hypodermic syringe 1853
- **heart-lung machine** 1953
- **kidney dialysis machine** 1944–5
- **sterilising machines** 1875+
- **TV for keyhole surgery** for 1990s

Items that are in **bold** rely on electricity.

❖ *If you had to pick a date at which 'high technology' began, what date would you choose?*
❖ *Choose the scientific discovery which you think was most important for medicine.*
   (a) Explain the medical improvements it led to.
   (b) Explain what technological developments were needed to make it work.

Marie Curie discovered radium in 1898

Thermometers

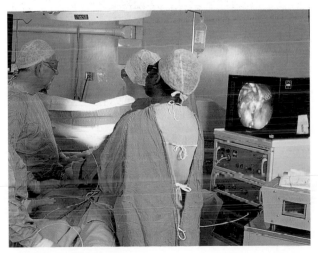

Keyhole surgery, 1992

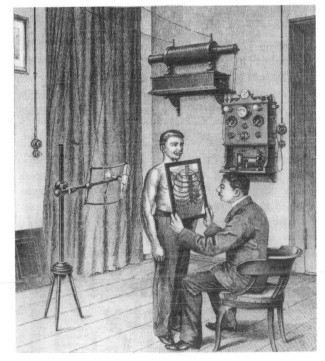

An X-ray photograph, 1903

111

WHY DO THINGS HAPPEN IN HISTORY?

On pages 78–111 we have looked at the effects of four factors on medical ideas and methods. But these are not the only factors affecting medicine. What other factors can you think of?

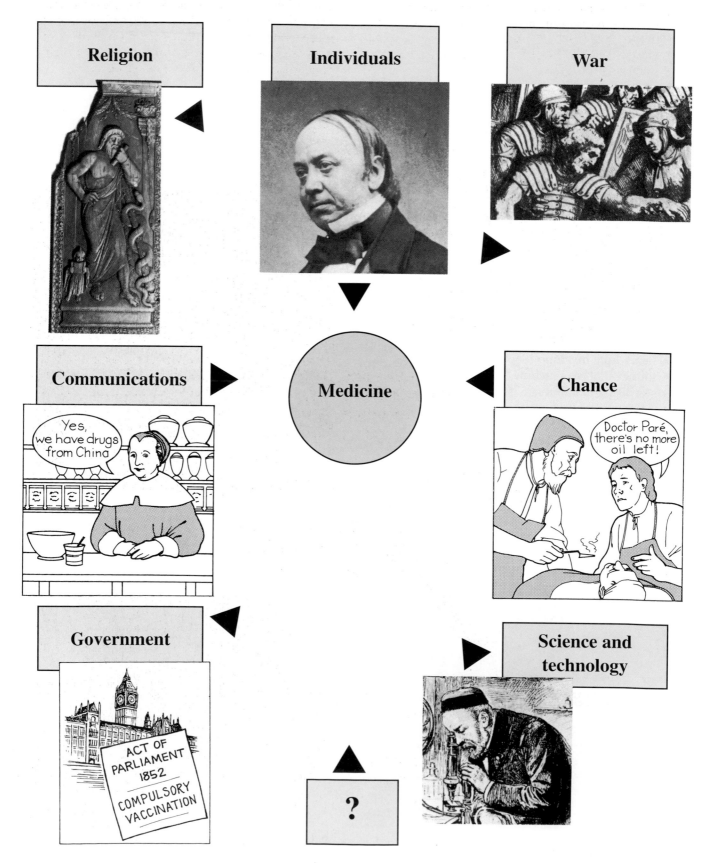

WHY DID IT HAPPEN THEN?

Another of the questions that historians ask about things that have happened is 'Why did it happen then?' They can see, for example, what factors caused the passing of the 1875 Public Health Act. But why is it the 1875 Public Health Act, not the 1865 Act, or the 1775 Act or the 1975 Act?

Look back over pages 92 to 95 to see what you think. What combination of factors was involved? How did they ensure that the Act was passed in that year and not any other? This **Issues and Enquiries** section goes on to look at four case studies of changes in medicine. In each case study you will examine the question: Why did it happen then?

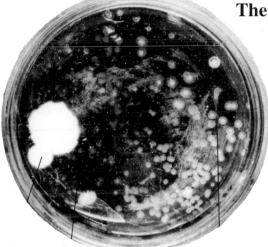

The development of penicillin

page114–125

Professional medical training for women

page126–133

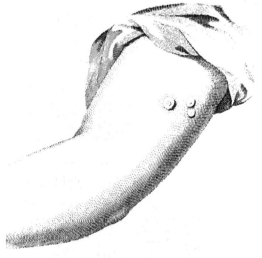

The development of vaccinations

page134–141

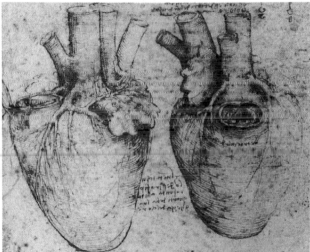

The medical Renaissance

page142–151

1 THE DEVELOPMENT OF PENICILLIN

SOURCE 1

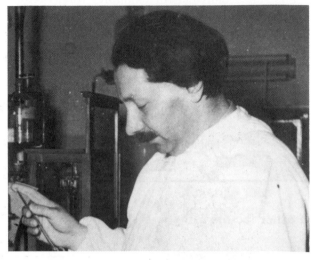

KEY QUESTION
◆ *What part did Chain, Fleming and Florey play in the discovery and development of penicillin?*

The development of penicillin

On pages 56 to 57 you read about 'magic bullets' – ways of killing germs inside the body. You probably remember the dramatic story in Source 1.

SOURCE 1 – Normally he would have died

We had enormous numbers of infected wounded, terrible burn cases among the crews of the armoured cars. Sulphonamides had absolutely no effect on these cases. The last thing I tried was penicillin. I had very little penicillin, something like 10 000 units, maybe less.

The first man I tried it on was a young New Zealand officer called Newton. He had been in bed for six months with compound fractures of both legs. His sheets were soaked with pus and the heat in Cairo made the smell intolerable. Normally he would have died in a short time. I gave three injections a day of penicillin and studied the effects under a microscope . . . The thing seemed like a miracle. In ten days time the left leg was cured and in a month's time the young fellow was back on his feet. I had enough penicillin left for ten cases. Nine of them were complete cures.

Lt. Col. Pulvertaft, an army doctor in North Africa, 1943, quoted in André Maurois, *Life of Sir Alexander Fleming*, 1959.

Three men who helped to develop penicillin: Ernst Chain (top); Alexander Fleming (middle); Howard Florey (bottom).

The story of the discovery and development of penicillin is told on pages 116 to 121 and again, as a cartoon, on pages 124 to 125. As you read through them, think about the factors which affected the story.

Other factors   Think about the other factors shown on this page. Clearly the work of Fleming, Florey and Chain was a factor of great importance.

KEY QUESTIONS
◆ *Were they all equally important?*
◆ *Fleming made the first discovery. Does that make him the most important?*

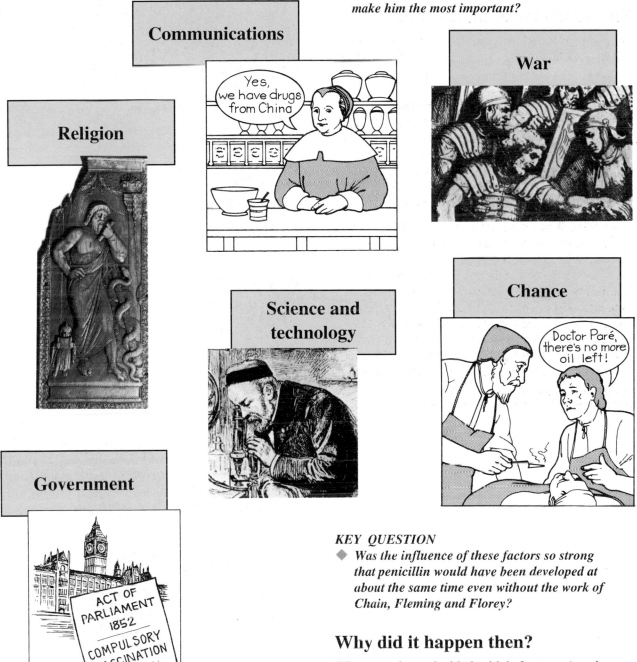

KEY QUESTION
◆ *Was the influence of these factors so strong that penicillin would have been developed at about the same time even without the work of Chain, Fleming and Florey?*

Why did it happen then?

When you have decided which factors played a part in the discovery and development of penicillin, look at the dates in the story.

KEY QUESTION
◆ *Why did these things happen then? Could the same discoveries and developments have been made: in 1870?*
    in 1917?
    in 1928?
    in the 1970s?

Fleming and penicillin

SOURCE 1

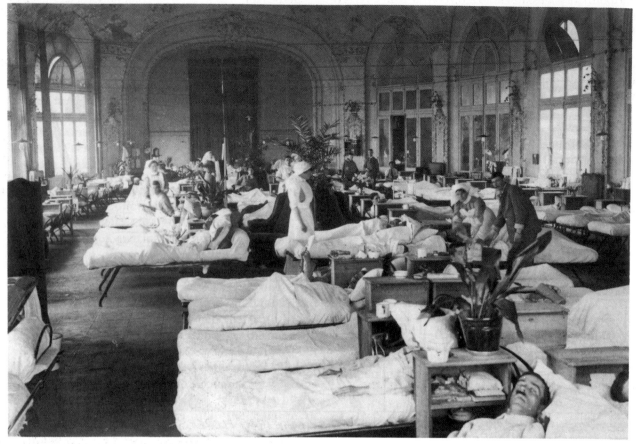

Surgical ward in the army hospital at Boulogne where Fleming worked 1914–18.

When cheese or fruit goes bad, the organism that grows on them is a mould with the Latin name 'penicillium'. The microscopic spores that spread the mould float in the air almost everywhere, including inside scientific laboratories. In 1871 some of them fell on to specimens growing in the lab of Joseph Lister, the discoverer of antiseptic surgery. Lister noticed that the mould seemed to weaken the microbes that he was studying at the time. He made experiments and tried using 'penicillium' on some of his patients (see Source 2, p.114), but he did not follow up the idea.

Seventy years later, in 1942–45, penicillin came into use. Like the other 'magic bullets' of the 20th century it could be injected so that it could kill germs deep inside the body. But it could kill a far wider range of germs than they could and it had fewer harmful effects. With penicillin, diseases and infections that used to lead to almost certain death could be cured in a few days. It seemed like magic.

Alexander Fleming

Fleming was born in Scotland in 1881 and he qualified as a doctor at St Mary's Hospital, London, in 1906.

He had been a successful student and he was offered a job as a bacteriologist at St Mary's under Sir Almroth Wright. This was a great honour for the young doctor. Wright had discovered typhoid vaccine in 1896 and was one of the leading British doctors. He believed that vaccines were the true answer to most diseases, and he tried for years to use them for treatment as well as for prevention. In St Mary's he set up an inoculation department, partly for research, partly to produce vaccines for general use.

A profitable factory was established inside the hospital. Since the time of Lister's experiments a whole new science of bacteriology had been built up by people like Pasteur and Koch. Many harmful germs had been identified, and the methods of killing them studied. Fleming's routine work for the next 40 years was largely to identify bacteria for doctors at the hospital, and to test vaccines by seeing which bacteria they killed or weakened. The method he used to grow the germs and to make tests on them had in the main been developed by Koch in Berlin in the 1880s, though Fleming and others made improvements of their own. The covered glass dish in which germs are grown is still called a Petri dish after one of Koch's assistants.

During the First World War, Wright and Fleming worked in a hospital for wounded soldiers in France. The bullets or shell fragments often carried dangerous germs deep into the soldiers' bodies, and Wright and Fleming studied the results. They were not popular with the other doctors when they proved that in cases like this the ordinary antiseptics did more harm than good – not that they could offer anything better (see Source 3).

Back in St Mary's Hospital after the war Fleming returned to his old routines. He was able also to follow up ideas for research, and in 1922 he made an important discovery – a substance in tears and other body fluids that kills many harmless germs, but not the germs that cause disease. Fleming wrote articles about it, but did not develop it. He was happy working in Wright's department where the main business was about vaccines, and he was not keen to branch out on his own.

SOURCE 2 – Penicillin in 1881

In 1940 a patient of Lister's described to Dr Fraser-Moore the treatment she had received in King's College Hospital in 1881, when she was a young nurse. Injured in a street accident, she sustained a wound that became infected. Various antiseptics failed to clear the infection and then something was used that worked so dramatically that she asked Lister's Registrar to write the name of it in her scrap book. The writing in her book, which she showed to Fraser-Moore, was Penicillium.

Dr G. McFarlane, *Fleming, the Man and the Myth*, 1985.

SOURCE 3 – We could do nothing to help

Surrounded by all these infected wounds, by men who were suffering and dying without our being able to do anything to help them, I was consumed by a desire to discover something which would kill those microbes, something like salvarsan.

Fleming, later memories quoted in André Maurois, *Life of Sir Alexander Fleming*, 1959

SOURCE 4

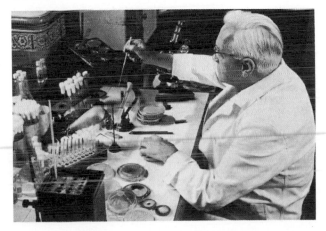

Fleming in his laboratory at St Mary's.

Fleming discovers penicillin

In 1928, Fleming was studying staphylococci – the germs that cause boils and spots. He had dozens of glass dishes in which they were growing. A stack of discarded dishes stood in a dish of disinfectant ready for cleaning. By chance a colleague dropped in for a chat and Fleming grumbled to him about the amount of work to be done. Some of the discarded dishes were still above the level of the disinfectant and Fleming picked up one or two as he spoke. It was then that he made his great discovery. Mould was growing on one of the dishes, as it usually did on old ones. But what Fleming noticed was that no germs were growing near the mould. 'That's funny!' he said, and picked off a tiny piece of mould and put it carefully in a dish of jelly where it could grow. Much of the penicillin that saved so many lives since 1942 was descended from that tiny piece of mould.

SOURCE 5

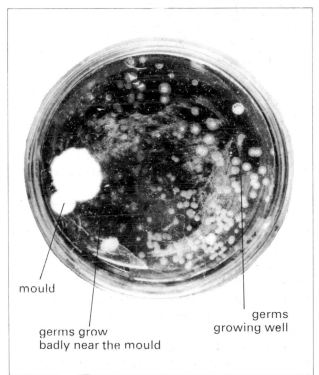

mould

germs grow
badly near the mould

germs
growing well

Photograph of the original dish showing the effect of penicillin.

❖ *Fleming kept this dish and had it photographed. Why do you think he did this?*

The mould could combat one disease germ. Could it combat others? Fleming tried it with a series of deadly bacteria. It worked with diphtheria. It worked with the bacteria that cause gangrene and meningitis. It worked with most, but not all of the bacteria causing serious infections. 'It looks as though we have a mould here that can do something useful,' he said.

Fleming was not an expert on moulds, so he asked a colleague who studied them in a laboratory on the floor below to identify it for him. It was one of the penicillium family, such as Lister had noticed nearly 60 years earlier. But Fleming's penicillium was such a rare member of the family that his colleague got the name wrong. How it came into Fleming's laboratory remains a mystery. Perhaps one of the spores had floated up or been carried up from the floor below at a moment when the cover was removed from that particular plate.

Fleming worked hard for a time on his mould. He tried other sorts of penicillium, without any success. He tried various ways of purifying the 'mould juice', but this turned out to need greater skill in chemistry than was available. He injected it into animals and showed that it did them no harm. He used it to cure a colleague's eye infection, and could see clearly that it was useful and that it did not harm to body tissues. But he found that it quickly lost its effectiveness, and did not seem to work when mixed with blood.

He wrote articles in 1929 and 1931 describing his work and naming the active substance 'penicillin', but after that he returned to his routine work. He kept a supply of the mould, because it was useful to identify germs and to test vaccines, but he did no more to develop it.

❖ *What part was played by chance in Fleming's discovery?*
❖ *What other factors that were not a matter of chance helped to bring about this discovery?*
❖ *What reasons can you suggest why Fleming did not follow up his discovery effectively?*

SOURCE 1 – Fleming's 1929 claim

It is suggested that penicillin may be an efficient antiseptic for application to or injection into areas infected with penicillin-sensitive microbes.

From Fleming's article of 1929 in the *British Journal of Experimental Pathology*.

SOURCE 2 – Fleming was extremely keen

He was well aware of the therapeutic potentialities of penicillin, and was extremely keen that it should be purified, because, he said, it was 'the only product capable of killing microbes such as the staphylococci, without injuring the white corpuscles'.

Dr L. Holt, a biochemist who worked with Fleming in 1934, later memories quoted in André Maurois, *Life of Sir Alexander Fleming*, 1959.

SOURCE 3 – History might have been changed

[Fleming had just been told of Lister's experiment of 1871 using a penicillium mould to kill bacteria.]
Fleming: 'What a pity that his experiment of November 1871 didn't come off. He had the idea of penicillin, but he had the wrong mould or the wrong bacteria or both. If fate had been kind to him medical history might have been changed and Lister might have lived to see what he had always been looking for – a non-poisonous antiseptic. From the time of Pasteur and Lister workers had been trying to kill one bacteria with another. The idea was there but the performance had to wait until Fortune decreed that a mould spore should contaminate one of my cultures, and then for a few years more until the chemists busied themselves with the products of this same mould to give us pure penicillin. Lister would indeed have rejoiced to have had such a thing.'

Fleming talking in the 1950s to Lord Webb-Johnson. André Maurois, *Life of Sir Alexander Fleming*, 1959.

Howard Florey and Ernst Chain

It was Florey and Chain who followed up Fleming's lead. In the years 1938–42 they found out how to make pure penicillin in large quantities and showed how it should be used.

❖ *What factors helped to bring about the development of penicillin in the years after 1938?*

❖ *What were the motives of Florey and Chain?*

❖ *How far did the work of Florey and his team depend on that of Fleming?*

❖ *Is it likely that penicillin might have been developed in much the same way even if neither Fleming nor Florey had ever lived?*

Howard Florey was born in 1898 in Adelaide, Australia. He trained as a doctor, won a scholarship to Oxford in 1922 and then began to work in medical research. He produced a remarkable stream of important discoveries and in 1935 he became Professor of Pathology at Oxford, in charge of a large research organisation.

A key member of Florey's team at Oxford was Ernst Chain, a brilliant biochemist. Chain, a German Jew, had fled to Britain from Hitler's persecution. The first subject they tackled together was lysozyme, the substance Fleming had found in tears in 1922. They showed exactly how it worked in killing bacteria. This was of no direct practical value, but as they were finishing work on it they decided to move on to a general study of other natural substances that killed bacteria. Chain set out to read all the articles he could find on the subject – there were 200 of them. One was Fleming's 1929 article on penicillin. To Chain this seemed the most promising line to follow. They had a supply of Fleming's mould at Oxford and he started work on it in 1938. The difficulties were formidable. Fleming himself had done no more work on penicillin, but several biochemists, some of them at St Mary's, had tried without success to purify the 'mould juice'.

In 1939 Florey decided to concentrate the resources of his whole team on penicillin. Why did he make this decision? He had no idea how important penicillin was to be in the war that began that September. What he could see clearly was that it followed on from his previous work, and that it was the sort of problem his team could solve. He threw himself into it with his usual energy. By a brilliant combined effort they had solved the main problems by May 1940 and had enough purified penicillin and knew enough about its effects to try the crucial experiment.

SOURCE 4 – Penicillin might be useful now war has begun.

I enclose some proposals that have a very practical bearing at the moment.

The properties of penicillin hold out promise of its finding practical application in the treatment of infections. In view of the great practical importance of the above mentioned bactericidal [germ-killing] agents it is proposed to prepare these substances in a purified form suitable for injection and to study their antiseptic action in living creatures.

Application from Florey to the Medical Research Council for money to finance penicillin research, 6 September 1939, three days after the outbreak of war.

On 25 May 1940, Florey injected eight mice with enough staphylococci to kill them. He then gave four of them varying doses of penicillin. By 3.30 am next morning all four of the unprotected mice were dead, while the other four were alive and well, though one died two days later.

SOURCE 5

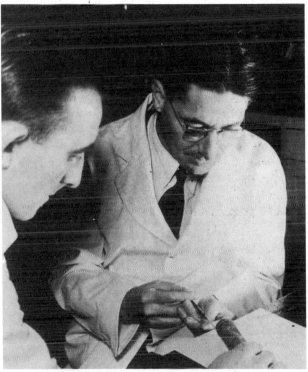

Florey injecting mice in the tail. The mice are held in a special tube.

Florey was a very unexcitable man, but he could see how important so clear a result might be. 'It looks like a miracle,' he told a friend on the phone. More typical was another remark, 'A man is 3000 times as big as a mouse': he needed a large quantity of penicillin to make tests on human beings. The whole research institute was turned into a penicillin factory. Bottles, tins and bed-pans from a nearby hospital were used to grow the mould, and Chain's apparatus to purify it. Florey asked for help from various drug manufacturers in Britain and the USA and even flew to America to explain what he needed. By February 1941 there was enough for the first human trial, on an Oxford policeman (see Source 1). Although the supply of penicillin ran out after four days and the patient died, it was clear how well it worked. Over the next two years, Florey, in a series of 187 cases, showed the enormous effectiveness of the drug, and worked out the best ways to use it.

It was during this period that two factors began to be of great importance. The first of these was the growth and power of the drug manufacturing industry. In the first forty years of the 20th century drug manufacture had become big business. In Germany, Britain and the USA a handful of large drug firms with well equipped research laboratories and massive factories dominated the market. They competed strongly with each other in their search for profit. If penicillin was to be made quickly in large quantities they were the only people who could make it. This is why Florey approached them in 1940. Some expressed interest, but at first they were cautious.

SOURCE 1

Fermentation tank used by Glaxo in the production of penicillin.

SOURCE 2 – The penicillin ran out and he died

The policeman had a sore on his mouth about a month previously, and the infection had spread to his scalp. He'd had an abscess there. It had spread to both his eyes and one had had to be removed. He had abscesses open on his arm. He had abscesses on his lung – he was well on his way towards death from the terrible infection. We'd nothing to lose and everything to gain. So we thought we'd have a try.

The shortage of penicillin was such that after the first day I collected all his urine and I took it over to where Florey was working so that the penicillin could be extracted from the urine and used again.

On the fourth day he was really dramatically improved. He was sitting up in bed and his temperature had gone down. On the fifth day the penicillin began to run out and we couldn't go on. Of course when they extracted it from the urine they couldn't get it all back and it gradually ran out. He wasn't cured. He gradually relapsed and eventually died.

Professor C. M. Fletcher, a member of Florey's team, speaking on *Horizon*, BBC TV, 27 January 1986.

The other factor was the war. Two days after Florey injected the mice, the British retreat from Dunkirk began. Britain's allies had all been beaten and she stood alone. 1940–41 was the time of the heaviest German air-raids on British cities. In December 1941 Japan sank the American fleet at Pearl Harbor and the USA entered the war. Penicillin could not have come at a better time. In both Britain and the USA government committees were set up to organise co-operation between the firms. Most of these, but not all, agreed to share the secrets they found. All agreed to produce as much as possible. Both governments agreed to buy as much as could be made. The US government even paid $75 million to help the companies to install expensive plant. In 1943 Florey went to Russia to explain how penicillin was made and used, and to give them samples. The Soviet Government set up plants to make it.

In 1943 Allied armies began to use it. By 1944 there was enough for all those wounded in the D-Day invasion of Europe to be treated. Penicillin had arrived.

SOURCE 3

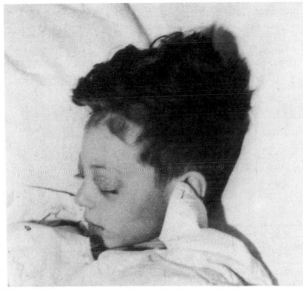

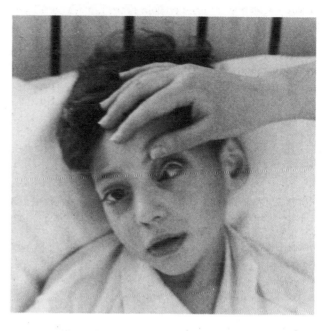

Little boy before (above) and after (right) penicillin. He was one of the first patients to be treated with penicillin, in 1941.

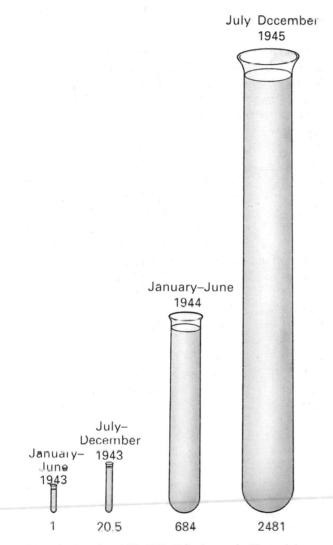

US production of penicillin 1943–45 (in thousand million units).

SOURCE 4 – We did it because it was interesting science

a. There are a lot of misconceptions about medical research. People sometimes think that I and the others worked on penicillin because we were interested in suffering humanity – I don't think it ever crossed our minds about suffering humanity; this was an interesting scientific exercise. Because it was some use in medicine was very gratifying but this was not the reason we started working on it. It might have been in the background of our minds – it's always in the background in people working on medical subjects – but that's not the mainspring.

Lord Florey in an interview in Australia, 1967

b. The only reason that motivated me was scientific interest. That penicillin could have a practical use in medicine did not enter our minds when we started work on it.

Sir Ernst Chain, *Journal of the Royal College of Physicians*, 1972

SOURCE 5 – Penicillin would have happened without Fleming or us

We would have started a research programme (into anti-bacterial substances provided by micro-organisms) even if Fleming's paper had never been published, and if we had not done so, someone else somewhere in the world would have taken this initiative. As a result some interesting anti-bacterial substances would have been discovered and a general screening programme would have started. This would undoubtedly have revealed the existence of the penicillin producing penicillia. The development of the antibiotic field might have been delayed a few years, but it would inevitably have taken place with the same final result we have now.

Ernst Chain, *Proceedings of the Royal Society*, 1971

The story of penicillin

1. WHEN FRUIT GOES BAD A MOULD GROWS ON IT CALLED PENICILLIUM. THIS MOULD IS SPREAD BY SPORES THAT FLOAT IN THE AIR.

2. IN 1871 SOME SPORES FLOATED INTO JOSEPH LISTER'S LABORATORY. HE NOTICED THAT THE MOULD WEAKENED THE GERMS HE WAS STUDYING BUT HE ONLY DID A FEW EXPERIMENTS, PERHAPS HE WAS TOO BUSY?

3. BY THE 1920s MANY SCIENTISTS WERE LOOKING FOR WAYS TO KILL GERMS. ONE WAS ALEXANDER FLEMING. HIS WORK WAS TO STUDY HOW VACCINES KILLED GERMS.

IT KILLS MANY DISEASE GERMS AND IT DOESN'T SEEM TO HARM THE BODY.

HOW CAN I TURN THE MOULD INTO A MEDICINE?

WHAT SHALL WE WORK ON NEXT?

6. FLEMING FOUND THAT THIS MOULD COULD KILL THE GERMS OF A NUMBER OF DISEASES AND CALLED IT PENICILLIN.

7. BUT HE DIDN'T DEVELOP THE IDEA - CHEMISTS WERE NEEDED TO MAKE THE MOULD USABLE AS A TREATMENT.

8. LATER OTHER PEOPLE READ ABOUT FLEMING'S WORK. HOWARD FLOREY WAS A PROFESSOR WITH A LARGE TEAM OF SCIENTISTS.

FIRST GIVE EIGHT MICE THE GERMS, THEN GIVE PENICILLIN TO FOUR OF THEM.

PENICILLIN WORKS - ON MICE AT LEAST. IT LOOKS LIKE A MIRACLE.

11. AN IMPORTANT EXPERIMENT.

12. LATER - FOUR DEAD MICE, FOUR LIVELY MICE.

13. WORK BEGAN TO MAKE MORE PENICILLIN AND TRY MORE EXPERIMENTS.

18. *IT SOUNDS A GOOD IDEA PROFESSOR, WE'LL LOOK AT THE COSTS.*

19. *WE NEED PENICILLIN TO WIN THE WAR. BUILD A NEW FACTORY - WE'LL HELP TO PAY.*

20. FLOREY VISITED RUSSIA TO PASS ON THE IDEAS.

PENICILLIN: WHO DESERVES THE CREDIT?

SOURCE 1

Fleming receiving the Nobel Prize from the King of Sweden, Gustavus V, 1945. Behind him is Ernst Chain.

Penicillin becomes famous

In August 1942, a London businessman, a friend of Fleming, was dying in St Mary's Hospital. Florey's Oxford results were already known to doctors, though not to the public in general, so Fleming rang Florey and asked him if he could spare some penicillin. Florey sent it straightaway, and by the end of the month the man was cured, to the astonishment of everybody in St Mary's. The papers picked up the story of this 'wonder drug', and the publicity about penicillin had begun.

In the summer of 1942 the war was going badly for Britain and her allies, and most of the news was bad. Perhaps this made people keen to know about this victory on the scientific front, and how it had come about. From this time until his death in 1955 the chief credit went to Fleming. He became a national hero in Britain and was honoured all over the world. After the war he travelled to many countries to be given honorary degrees and medals and to be received by kings and presidents. Florey and Chain were honoured too, and in 1945 the Nobel Prize was given to all three of them jointly. But somehow far more of the fame went to Fleming. Some doctors and scientists thought that this was unfair.

After 1942, when everybody knew how important penicillin was, it was easy for them to believe that Fleming had foreseen this and had actually been looking for it ever since his experiences in the First World War. Some doctors and scientists who were admirers of Florey have argued that this gives a distorted view of history.

SOURCE 2 – To the editor of *The Times*, 28 August 1942

Sir, In the leading article on penicillin yesterday, you refrained from putting the laurel wreath for discovery round anybody's brow. It should be given to Professor Alexander Fleming of this research laboratory. For he is the discoverer of penicillin and was the author also of the original suggestion that the substance might prove to have important applications in medicine.

I am, Sir, yours faithfully,
Almroth Wright,
Inoculation Department
St Mary's Hospital.

The Times, 31 August 1942

SOURCE 3 – The news is being twisted

I have now quite good evidence, from the Director General of the BBC in fact, and also indication from some people at St Mary's that Fleming is doing his best to see the whole subject is being presented as being foreseen and worked out by Fleming, and that we in this department just did a few final flourishes.

Letter from Florey to Sir Henry Dale, President of the Royal Society, 11 December 1942

SOURCE 4 – In 1928 I had no idea

Nothing is more certain than that when in September 1928 I saw bacteria fading away in the neighbourhood of a mould, I had no suspicion that I had got a clue to the most powerful substance yet used to defeat bacterial infection of the human body.

(Fleming, 13 December 1943, speaking to the American Pharmaceutical Manufacturers Association)

SOURCE 5 – Fleming gets too much publicity – Florey

My policy here has been never to interview the press or allow them to get any information from us by telephone. This has been rigidly adhered to in spite of protests from some of my colleagues (especially Chain).

In contrast Fleming has been interviewed apparently without cease, photographed, etc. (we have ample evidence of this here) with the upshot he is put across as the discoverer of penicillin (which is true), with the implication that he did all the work leading to the discovery of its properties (which is not true).

Many of my colleagues feel things are going much too far, and are getting naturally restive at seeing so much of their own work going to glorify or even financially enrich someone else.

Letter from Florey to the Secretary of the Medical Research Council, January 1944

SOURCE 6 – Fleming: one of the world's greatest scientists of all time

The man who made possible this incalculable alleviation of human suffering is Dr Alexander Fleming, discoverer of the anti-bacterial effect of the mould from which penicillin is made. He is a short, retiring Scot with somewhat dreamy blue eyes, fierce white hair and a mind which when it moves, moves like a cobra. It will be hard to say who the great men of the 20th century are, but Dr Alexander Fleming is certainly one of them. He belongs in the tradition of the scientific seers which includes Galileo and Isaac Newton.

Penicillin is already big business, yet Dr Fleming (who discovered it) and Dr Florey (who made it tick) have got nothing out of it but praise.

Time magazine, USA, 15 May 1944

SOURCE 7 – Fleming, a modest genius

When a man of genius is modest and simple the world is liable to undervalue what he has done. Alexander Fleming was a genius of this rare kind. During his life in his own land recognition of his genius was grudging. I became indignant on his behalf. I was anxious that justice should be done to this great pioneer. It seemed to me that it was a duty laid on me as the proprietor of newspapers in Britain, the country which gained a measure of reflected glory on account of Fleming's immense achievement.

(Lord Beaverbrook, Evening Standard, 5 January 1956. Beaverbrook owned the Daily Express and other papers. He was a friend of Fleming's boss Sir Almroth Wright, and had given large sums to St Mary's Hospital.)

SOURCE 8 – Fleming didn't deserve it

Fleming told me often that he didn't deserve the Nobel Prize, and I had to bite my teeth not to agree with him. He wasn't putting on an act – at least around 1945/6. At the same time he would tell me that he couldn't help enjoying all his undeserved fame and I liked him for that. With me and others of his scientific colleagues he had the sense to know that none of us were more impressed by him than he was himself.

Letter, Dr W. E. van Heuningen to Dr G. McFarlane, 3 August 1980, from *Alexander Fleming, the Man and the Myth*, 1984.

QUESTIONS

1. How does Source 1 appear to show that the main credit went to Fleming in 1945?

2. Almroth Wright (Source 2) does not mention Florey and his team at all. How can this be explained?

3. (a) Compare the interpretation of the discovery in Source 2 with the one in Source 8.
   (b) How can this difference of interpretation be explained?

4. How reliable is the evidence of Lord Beaverbrook (Source 7) in deciding on Fleming's role in the discovery of penicillin? Explain your answer.

5. Use Source 5 to suggest one reason for the dispute.

6. (a) Is the question, 'Who deserves the credit?' an important one for historians? Explain your answer.

   (b) Use the information on pages 114 to 125 to write your own answer to the question.

2 PROFESSIONAL MEDICAL TRAINING FOR WOMEN

KEY QUESTIONS

◆ *How important was the contribution of pioneers like Florence Nightingale or Elizabeth Garrett to the growth of professional training for women?*

◆ *What other factors helped to start this important change in the 19th century?*

◆ *Why did men oppose the training of women nurses and doctors in the 19th century?*

Women have always played a very important part in medical care. Yet as we have seen (pages 40–41) in early 19th-century Europe all medical professionals were men. Women could not train to be doctors – and as for nurses . . .

SOURCE 1 – Too bad to do anything else

Nursing was generally done by those who were too old, too weak, too drunk, too dirty, too stupid or too bad to do anything else.

Florence Nightingale, letter, 19 June 1867

By the end of the 19th century this situation had changed.

SOURCE 2 – Every girl wants to be a nurse

Every girl in her teens wants to be a nurse. Unless she contracts an early marriage, she casts longing eyes on the hospital ward whenever her home becomes dull and dances fail to satisfy the mind.

(Burdett's Hospital Annual, 1891–92)

In 1900 many women had trained and qualified as nurses, and a few had become doctors. Less than 1 per cent of the doctors in England and Wales were women, but an important change had begun. Why did it happen when it did?

One important factor was the general change in the position of women that began in the 19th century and continues in the 20th century. Women demanded and obtained the right to study in universities, to vote, and to work in many jobs on more equal terms with men. It is not surprising that this movement of 'Women's Emancipation' encouraged women to insist on their right to professional training in medicine.

This section looks at two case-studies in the growth of professional training for women in medicine:
• hospital nursing
• women as doctors.

Religion

Communications

Yes, we have drugs from China

War

Science and technology

Individuals

Chance

Doctor Paré, there's no more oil left!

Government

ACT OF PARLIAMENT 1852 COMPULSORY VACCINATION

CASE STUDY 1 Hospital nursing

Nursing in the early 19th century Until the late 19th century hospitals were places for the poor who could not afford to be looked after at home when they were ill. Few effective medical treatments were available, so nurses had few special skills.

Look at the sources on this page

❖ *What evidence is there about:*
  – the skills nurses needed
  – the quality of nursing they did
  – people's attitudes to nursing
  and nurses?

SOURCE 3

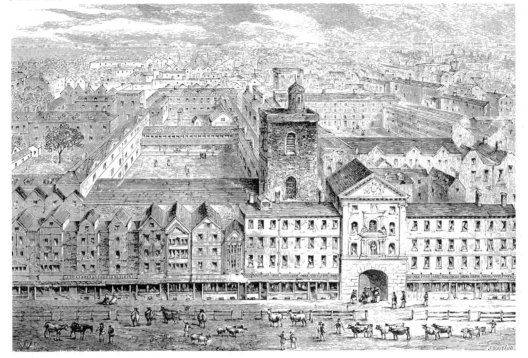

St Bartholomew's Hospital, London in 1750, from a contemporary drawing. St Bartholomew's dates back to 1123. During the 18th century eleven new hospitals were founded in London and 46 in other parts of Britain. The patients were mostly poor people and treatment was free. Patients going into St Bartholomew's had to pay a burial fee in case they died. If they recovered it was paid back to them.

SOURCE 4 – Immoral and cruel nurses

A nurse must possess considerable physical strength to lift the patients, sit up all night, etc. But who are the able-bodied women who are to be found in the workhouse and can obtain no paid work as servants elsewhere? Alas, there is one class! It is among the most depraved and immoral members of the community that the poor decent woman who has come to suffer and perhaps to die in the workhouse must find her sole attendant, too often her rough and cruel tyrant. A hard and unfeeling nurse may torment her patient. She moves her roughly when every touch is agony, she gives her her food cold, she monopolises for herself the easy chairs or bed-rests any kind visitor may have provided. When the wretched sufferer reaches the last stage she refuses (as we have witnessed) to give her the cold workhouse tea she craves for, to save herself the trouble of the arrangements.

Frances Cobbe, workhouse visitor, 1861. In 1834 a new system of workhouses was set up in Britain. The worst conditions and the worst nurses were in the workhouse infirmaries.

SOURCE 5 – Some nurses were clever and kind

Some of the nurses were of the best type of women, clever, dutiful, cheerful and kind, and endowed above all with that motherliness of nature which is the most precious attribute of a nurse.

Miss Pringle, a hospital matron, *Edinburgh Medical Journal*, May 1880

SOURCE 6 – Nurses slept on the landing

The nurses slept in wooden cages on the landing places outside the doors of the wards, where it was impossible for any woman of character to sleep, where it was impossible for the night nurse taking her rest in the day to sleep at all owing to the noise, where there was not light and air.

Florence Nightingale, letter, 19 May 1854

SOURCE 7 – All nurses drunken

In the course of her long experience she had never known a nurse who was not drunken, and there was immoral conduct and practice in the very wards, of which she gave awful examples.

Head nurse of a London hospital, reported by Florence Nightingale, 1854.

127

The Florence Nightingale story

Florence Nightingale

Florence Nightingale was born in 1820. Her parents were rich, and she and her elder sister were educated at home by governesses and by their father. Florence was intelligent, lively and attractive, and it seemed as if she would soon find a husband – the only acceptable future for a girl of the English upper classes at the time.

But Florence turned down several very eligible young men, and determined to devote her life to a higher purpose.

SOURCE 1 – What useful things have I done?

What have I done in this world and what have I done in the last fortnight? I have read to Papa (and) Mamma. Learnt several tunes by heart. Written various letters. Ridden with Papa. Paid eight visits. Done company [received visitors] and that is all.

(Florence Nightingale, 7 July 1849)

Florence was allowed to do one useful thing – to visit the cottages of the poor when people were sick. Here she saw real poverty and distress and a desperate need for help. Nursing, she decided, was the answer to her search for a sense of purpose. In 1844 she made her decision. 'Since the age of 24,' she wrote later, 'there was never any vagueness in my plans or ideas as to what God's work was for me.'

Her parents were horrified and it took her seven years to persuade them to agree. She quarrelled bitterly with her mother and elder sister over this, but her father gave her some support, and in 1851 she was allowed to go for training to Kaiserwerth in Germany. A small hospital there was run by a religious organisation. 'The nursing there was nil, and the hygiene was horrible, but I never met anyone with a higher tone or purer devotion,' wrote Florence many years later (see Source 3).

Her father now made her an allowance of £500 a year, and she was able to undergo more training and to study nursing and hospital management in Paris. In 1853 she was appointed matron of the Sanatorium for Sick Governesses in London. Her mother was ashamed of her daughter's job.

At the Sanatorium, Florence saw what a complete lack there was of reliable and trained nurses. She visited the London hospitals and studied the conditions there. She was more convinced than ever of the need for trained and disciplined nurses.

SOURCE 2

Florence Nightingale aged about 20. A drawing by her sister.

SOURCE 3 – Hard work, but now I know what it is to live

Until yesterday I had never had time to send my things to the wash. We have ten minutes for each of our meals, of which we have four. We get up at five; breakfast a quarter before six. The patients dine at eleven; the sisters at twelve. Several evenings a week we collect in the great hall for a bible lesson.

I find the deepest interest in everything here and am so well in body and mind. This is life. Now I know what it is to live and to love life. I wish for no other world, no other earth than this.

(Letter from Florence to her mother, July 1851)

The Crimean War makes Florence a heroine

In 1854, Britain and France and Turkey invaded the Crimea in southern Russia. The telegraph and the steam ship had recently been invented, so this was the first war of which news could be sent home within a day or so of a battle. *The Times* newspaper sent William Russell to report on the battles – the first war correspondent. In the Crimean War, for the first time people at home could read in their morning papers of the horrors suffered by wounded soldiers.

In 1854 the British military hospital at Scutari in Turkey was swamped by a flood of wounded men. Conditions were dreadful, with blocked sewers, no trained nurses, no blankets and no bandages (see Source 1). The wounded soldiers died like flies. Russell's reports caused a public outcry. The government would have to take action.

Source 1 – The public will be angry

Scutari, 12th October 1854

It is with feelings of surprise and anger that the public will learn that no sufficient preparations have been made for the care of the wounded. Not only are there not sufficient surgeons, not only are there no dressers or male nurses, there is not even linen to make bandages. The men are kept, in some cases for a week, without the hand of a medical man coming near their wounds. They are left to expire in agony, unheeded and shaken off, though catching desperately at the surgeon whenever he makes his rounds. Now, when they have been placed in this spacious building, [a large barracks at Scutari, Turkey] it is found that the commonest appliances of a workhouse sick ward are lacking. The French have the help of the Sisters of Charity who are excellent nurses.

The Times, **14 October 1854**

The cabinet minister responsible for conditions in the army was Sidney Herbert, a personal friend of the Nightingale family, who knew Florence well. He wrote to ask her to help (Source 3).

Florence agreed immediately and took four trained nurses with hospital experience and 24 nuns to Scutari. At first the army doctors bitterly opposed them, but gradually they saw how useful they were. The death rate in the hospital fell from 42 per cent to 2 per cent in the two years that they were there. The wounded soldiers and the public at home put the whole of this improvement down to the work of Florence and her nurses, though many factors were involved. But when Florence came home at the end of the war the public subscribed £50 000 (the equivalent of several million pounds today) to set up a 'Nightingale School of Nursing', as a reward.

SOURCE 3 – There is only one person in England able to put things right

Dear Miss Nightingale,
You will have seen in the papers that there is a great deficiency of nurses in the Hospital at Scutari. I am confident that female nurses might be introduced with great benefit, for hospital orderlies must be very rough hands and most of them very inexperienced ones.

I receive numbers of offers from ladies to go out, but they are ladies who have no conception of what a hospital is, and they would be entirely useless and entirely in the way.

There is but one person in England that I know of who would be capable of organising and superintending such a scheme. Would you listen to a request to go and superintend the whole thing? I know that you will come to a wise decision.
Believe me, dear Miss Nightingale.
ever yours,
Sidney Herbert.

Letter, 15 October 1854, from Sidney Herbert to Florence Nightingale

SOURCE 2

Military hospital at Sebastapol before the nurses arrived.

The Nightingale School creates a new profession

The Nightingale School at St Thomas' Hospital, London, created the modern nursing profession. It started in 1860 with 15 student nurses, but Nightingale nurses soon went on to become matrons or to run training schools in other hospitals. By 1887 Nightingale nurses had gone to work in Australia, Canada, India, Ceylon, Germany, Sweden and the USA. Sixteen hospitals in Britain at that time had matrons trained in the Nightingale School. In 1901 there were in Britain 2000 student nurses, 3170 trained nurses in hospitals, and many thousands of others working in home nursing.

Opposition to training nurses

A few doctors opposed the training of nurses. In 1857 the President of the Royal College of Surgeons was Mr J. F. South. He argued that the new training was not needed.

SOURCE 4 – Nurses need no more training than housemaids

I am not at all disposed to allow that the nursing establishments of our hospitals are inefficient, or that they are likely to be improved by any special institution for training . . . Nurses are in much the same position as housemaids and require little teaching beyond that of poultice-making which is easily acquired, the enforcement of cleanliness and attention to the patients' wants. This proposed hospital nurse training scheme has not met with the support of the medical profession.

J. F. South, *Facts relating to Hospital Nurses*, 1857

SOURCE 5 – Operations in the kitchen

Dear Sir,
The use of the ward kitchens for operations and surgical appliances has been a source of great discomfort to the sisters and nurses.

Possibly the surgeons have not fully understood that these kitchens are the general dining rooms for the sisters and nurses, that all their food is kept in them and that they are also used for the preparation of the patients' breakfasts, tea etc.

I hope that you will kindly bring the subject before the surgeons and that we may be relieved of this revolting cause of discontent.
I have the honour to be,
Dear Sir,
Yours faithfully,
S. E. Wardroper
(Matron of St Thomas' Hospital, London)

Letter to the hospital's Senior Surgeon, Mr J. F. South, writer of Source 4, 1856

Twenty years later no up-to-date surgeon could have written like Mr South (Source 4) or behaved as described in Source 5.

❖ *What new development in medicine helped to end these attitudes, and make properly trained nurses essential?*

SOURCE 6

The Scutari hospital after Florence Nightingale had improved it.

CASE STUDY 2   Women as doctors

By the 19th century the few women doctors of earlier times had been forgotten, and all doctors in the advanced countries were men. So were most other people in positions of power. It was a man's world, in which a woman's place was in the home looking after the children, or working at a humble job like that of a servant.

A tiny minority of women protested about this and about 1850 one or two of them determined to become doctors. They faced formidable difficulties. For instance science was now essential for the study of medicine and very few girls learned any science at all. Until the 1850s there were hardly any secondary schools for girls. Even more serious, the world of medical students was an all-male one. They were used to coarse jokes and rowdy behaviour. This was at a time when young ladies of the richer classes were taught to be refined and delicate.

The first woman in modern times to qualify as a doctor was Elizabeth Blackwell, an American teacher. She taught herself enough basic science and saved enough money to pay for her course in medical school. Most medical schools refused to admit her because she was a woman, but finally she applied to a small college in the state of New York. The country students were not so used to fine ladies as those of the city colleges. The professors asked the students for their opinion and they voted to accept Elizabeth. She was a good student and she qualified in 1849. At first she found it hard to find work, but in 1853 she set up a successful clinic in New York for poor women and children.

❖ *Why should the poor be more ready to accept women doctors than the rich?*

The opposition to women medical students was much stronger in the well-established medical schools and universities of Europe than in a small American college. But in the 1850s a few determined women in Britain were beginning to campaign for greater equality of the sexes. In 1859 Dr Blackwell, whose work had by now made her famous, travelled to Europe. One of those who met her in England was Elizabeth Garrett. Aged 24, she had a good education, plenty of money and some support from her father. She determined to follow Dr Blackwell's example and qualify as a doctor. At first her father was horrified (see Source 2).

SOURCE 1

Elizabeth Garrett Anderson, 1870.

SOURCE 2 – Father thinks the idea is disgusting

I have just concluded a satisfactory talk with father on the medical subject. He does not like it, I think. He said the whole idea was disgusting and he could not entertain it for a moment. I asked what there was to make doctoring more disgusting than nursing, which women were also doing and which ladies had done publicly in the Crimea. He could not tell me . . . I think he will probably come round in time. I mean to renew the subject pretty often.

Letter from Elizabeth Garrett to her friend Emily Davies, 1859

SOURCE 3

Young Reginald de Braces has succeeded in catching a bad cold in order that he might send for that rising practitioner Dr Arabella Bolus. Cartoon from *Punch*, 1865.

❖ *Would this cartoon be likely to help or hinder the acceptance of women doctors?*

SOURCE 4 – The presence of young females is an outrage on our instincts

We the undersigned students consider that the mixture of the sexes in the same class is likely to lead to results of an unpleasant character.

The lecturers are likely to feel some restraint through the presence of females in giving that explicit and forcible enunciation of some facts which is necessary.

The presence of young females as spectators in the operating theatre is an outrage on our natural instincts and feelings and calculated to destroy those sentiments of respect and admiration with which the sex is regarded by all right-minded men. Such feelings are a mark of civilisation and refinement.

Statement of students at the Middlesex Hospital, London, 13 June 1861. As a result Elizabeth was not allowed to attend the lectures, so she continued to study privately.

SOURCE 5

A French cartoon from *Frou-Frou*, pre-1920. 'Esculape' is the French form of Asklepios. The girl is wearing robes similar to those worn by doctors when they qualified.

❖ *Was the cartoonist in favour of women doctors or against them?*

Later Mr Garrett changed his mind. He helped his daughter first to work as a nurse and attend medical lectures, and then to take private lessons from leading medical teachers. It was much more difficult to gain acceptance from the students (see Source 4).

Elizabeth passed all her exams, but to be allowed to work as a doctor she had a further problem. In 1858 medical qualifications in Britain had been regulated by law. Every new doctor had to be accepted as a member of the College of Physicians, the College of Surgeons, or the Society of Apothecaries. The first two of these had clear rules against women members and the third was very reluctant to accept Elizabeth. So in 1865 she and her father brought a legal case against the Society and forced it to accept her. Afterwards the Society changed its rules so as to prevent other women following her example. Elizabeth was now at last able to work as a doctor, but it took her another five years to complete her qualification by becoming a Doctor of Medicine. No British university would accept her, so she studied French and became a Doctor of Medicine of the University of Paris in 1870.

By this time girls' education was beginning to improve. Several universities were beginning to admit women, and in 1874 six women led by Sophia Jex-Blake completed a full medical course at Edinburgh. The university immediately announced that it was only permitted to grant medical degrees to men. Sophia and her friends completed their degrees at Dublin or at Zurich. Meanwhile they founded the London School of Medicine for Women in 1874. In 1876 Parliament passed an act that opened all medical qualifications to women. Even this did not end the resistance of existing doctors. For instance during the years 1876–81 the Royal College of Surgeons refused to examine anyone in midwifery, so as to avoid having to examine women.

The fact that women were able to qualify as doctors does not mean that many did so. Even in 1992 only 24 per cent of doctors in England and Wales were women. In the 1990s over half the students starting to study medicine are women, but 45 per cent of those who qualify give up the job within five years, compared with only 10 per cent of the men.

❖ *What factors made it difficult for women to become doctors in the 19th century?*
❖ *Why should the percentage of doctors who are women remain low in late 20th-century Britain?*

3 THE DEVELOPMENT OF VACCINATIONS

KEY QUESTIONS

◆ *What factors made it possible to develop vaccination in 18th-century Britain and later in 19th-century France?*

◆ *What other factors had to come into play before vaccination could really overcome smallpox?*

◆ *Why was there such a long delay between Jenner's discovery and Pasteur's developments?*

◆ *Is it likely that other people at the time might have made the same discoveries if Jenner or Pasteur had not done so?*

◆ *What part did chance play in these discoveries?*

Most children in Britain today are protected against certain diseases by vaccination. This was first developed against smallpox by Edward Jenner, a Gloucestershire doctor, in 1798. Nearly a hundred years later Louis Pasteur developed vaccinations against other diseases, and others later followed his lead. Today vaccinations save countless lives. Why did this important development happen when it did?

Smallpox

SOURCE 1

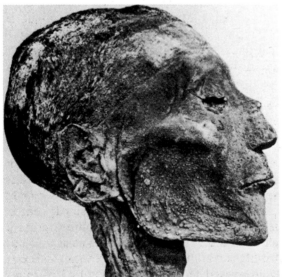

Mummy of Ramses V, ruler of Egypt, c.1160 BC, showing marks of smallpox.

SOURCE 2 – How to recognise smallpox

Before smallpox breaks out the patient has a continued fever, pain in the back, itching inthe nose and terrors in sleep. Signs that it is getting nearer are a pain in the throat and chest, a slight difficulty in breathing and a cough, a dryness of the mouth, thick spittle, hoarseness, headache, distress of mind, nausea and anxiety.

As soon as the symptoms appear, drop rose water in the eyes. The patient should gargle with pomegranate juice.

Rhazes, Baghdad, C AD 925

Smallpox has been known for thousands of years. There are no reliable figures before the 19th century, but like other epidemic diseases it seems to have varied in strength. It was particularly bad in Europe in the 18th century. Over nine out of ten people caught it, and of those who did, more than one in ten died of it. Others were often disfigured for life.

SOURCE 3

A few months old and already they've got enemies.

Health Education Authority poster, 1996. In Britain vaccination (or immunisation) against diphtheria, whooping cough, tetanus, polio, measles, rubella (german measles), Hib infection (a form of meningitis) and tuberculosis (TB) is available, free, to all children.

Inoculation – an early method of tackling smallpox

People had known for a long time that it was very unusual to catch some diseases twice.

For centuries the Chinese had protected themselves against the more serious forms of smallpox by deliberately spreading the milder ones. They did this by 'inoculation'. They took some of the matter from a smallpox spot or 'pustule' on a person with a mild attack. Then they scratched a healthy person and put the smallpox matter into the scratch.

In the early 18th century this method was well known in Turkey (see Source 4). It was brought to England by Lady Mary Wortley Montagu, wife of the British Ambassador there. When she returned home she persuaded the Princess of Wales to have her children inoculated. A test was first made on six orphans and when they survived the royal children were successfully inoculated. This helped to make the technique popular. By Jenner's time it was quite well known; he himself had been inoculated with smallpox as a boy.

A serious problem with inoculation was that it was impossible to be certain that mild smallpox would stay mild. Sometimes it had mild effects on one person and then killed somebody else or disfigured them badly.

SOURCE 4 – Inoculation in Turkey

The smallpox is here entirely harmless by the invention of engrafting. There is a set of old women who make it their business. Every autumn people send to each other to know if any of their family has a mind to have the smallpox. They make parties for this. the old woman comes with a nut shell full of the matter of the best smallpox and asks what vein you would like to have opened. She immediately rips open the one you offer to her with a large needle, and put into the vein as much venom as can lie on the head of the needle, and afterwards binds up the wound. The children play together all the rest of the day and are in perfect health for eight days. Then the fever begins, and they keep to their beds two days, very seldom three. They have rarely above 20 or 30 spots in their faces, which never mark permanently. In eight days time they are as well as before the illness. Every year thousands undergo this operation.

I should write about it to some of our doctors in England if I knew one of them that I thought would destroy a considerable branch of their income for the good of mankind. Perhaps if I live to return I may have courage to do battle with the doctors.

Lady Mary Wortley Montagu, letter to a friend, 1 April 1717

SOURCE 5 – Inoculators make a profit

The Suttons in eleven years inoculated 2514 people, for substantial fees. They also sold, for anything between fifty and a hundred pounds, to doctors living at a safe distance from them, the secrets of their methods. They had their own inoculation house at Ingatestone in Essex where patients were prepared for the operation and rested after it.

Dorothy Fisk, *Doctor Jenner of Berkeley*, 1959

SOURCE 6 – Everybody should be inoculated

Few people would choose even to hire a servant who had not had smallpox, far less purchase a slave who had the chance of dying from the disease. How could a physician or a surgeon who had never had the smallpox attend others with that malady?

I have often wished to see some plan established for rendering the practice (of inoculation) universal.

Dr W. Buchan, *Domestic Medicine*, 1769. Over 80 000 copies of this book were sold.)

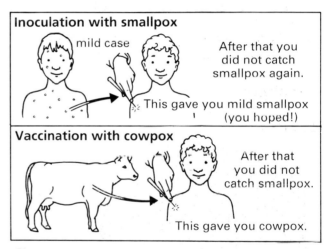

Inoculation with smallpox
mild case
After that you did not catch smallpox again.
This gave you mild smallpox (you hoped!)

Vaccination with cowpox
After that you did not catch smallpox.
This gave you cowpox.

Cowpox

Cowpox is a disease in which cattle develop 'pustules' very much like the smallpox spots on human beings. It was quite well known in 18th-century England, and many people knew that people who had had cowpox did not usually catch smallpox. One example was Thomas Jesty, a Wiltshire farmer. He had had cowpox as a child. Two of his servants had also had cowpox and later they had nursed relatives with smallpox without catching it themselves. In 1774 he took his wife and two children to a cow with the disease, scratched their arms and rubbed in matter from the pustules on the cow. All three caught cowpox, and Mrs Jesty was very ill. The neighbours blamed Jesty for this and although she recovered, he appears to have kept quiet about what he had done. A local clergyman was told the story in 1802, when Jenner's success was already known.

Edward Jenner develops vaccination

SOURCE 1

Edward Jenner

Vaccination against smallpox was developed by Edward Jenner in England in the 1790s. Why did this happen at that time and place?

❖ *Inoculation was known in China and Turkey long before it was known in Britain. What factors might explain why vaccination was developed first in Britain?*

❖ *Were these factors so strong that somebody else would probably have discovered it even without Jenner?*

❖ *Why is Jenner looked on as the discoverer and not Farmer Jesty? (see page 135)*

Jenner was born in Berkeley, Gloucestershire, in 1749. He worked for a time as apprentice to a local surgeon and then, at the age of 21, he went to London to study under the most famous surgeon of the time, John Hunter. Hunter was one of the first scientific surgeons. He made many experiments and encouraged his students to make careful observation and to record their results precisely.

In 1773 Jenner went back to Berkeley and set up as the local doctor. He followed up his scientific interests by observing the natural world around him, and in 1788 he was made a Fellow of the Royal Society. He also took a special interest in the cowpox stories that he heard.

Cowpox was not a very common disease. Most doctors were rather scornful of the village gossip about it and nobody before Jenner had attempted to describe it and its effects scientifically.

In 1796–98 Jenner found some infected cows and carried out his investigation. His aim was to prove two things:

a. that somebody who had had cowpox could not catch smallpox.

b. that by using matter from a cowpox pustule on one person, the disease could be passed on to another. Sources 3 and 5 show how well he succeeded.

Opposition to Jenner

Jenner's book was published in 1798. He was only a country doctor, and most leading doctors in London did not accept his ideas, though some did. Neither Jenner nor anyone else could offer any explanation of how vaccination worked. In spite of this, his methods were copied all over Britain. Many of the doctors and others who copied him took far less care than Jenner. There was at this time no knowledge that germs cause infection, and there were no antiseptics, so things often went wrong. One doctor, for instance, vaccinated patients in the same room as he inoculated others with smallpox. It was easy to get the diseases mixed up, and as a result patients often died.

In spite of this opposition, vaccination was gradually accepted. Jenner was supported by the King and given a reward of £30 000 by Parliament. Within a few years people were being vaccinated successfully in countries as far apart as India and Mexico. Jenner became world famous.

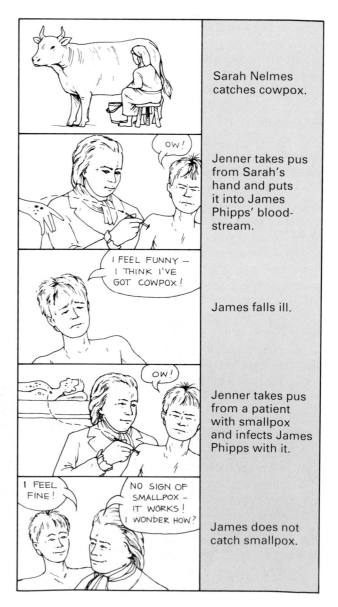

Sarah Nelmes catches cowpox.

Jenner takes pus from Sarah's hand and puts it into James Phipps' bloodstream.

James falls ill.

Jenner takes pus from a patient with smallpox and infects James Phipps with it.

James does not catch smallpox.

SOURCE 2 – I couldn't give them smallpox

My attention was first excited by observing that among those whom in the country I was frequently called upon to inoculate, many resisted every attempt to give them the smallpox. These patients I found had undergone a disease they called the cowpox, contracted by milking cows. On enquiry it appeared that it had been known from time immemorial, and that a vague opinion prevailed that it was a preventative of the smallpox.

Edward Jenner, *The Origin of the Vaccine Inoculation*, 1801

SOURCE 3 – Dr Jenner's case-book

Case 1. Sarah Nelmes, a dairymaid near this place, was infected with the cowpox from her master's cows in May 1796. A large sore and the usual symptoms were produced. I have given a representation of the pustule in the annexed plate.

Sarah Nelmes's arm.

Case 17. James Phipps. I selected a healthy boy, about eight years old. The matter was taken from the sore on the hand of Sarah Nelmes and it was inserted on 14 May 1796 into the arm of the boy by two cuts each about half an inch long. On the seventh day he complained of uneasiness, on the ninth he became a little chilly, lost his appetite and had a slight headache and spent the night with some degree of restlessness, but on the day following he was perfectly well.

In order to ascertain whether the boy was secure from the contagion of the smallpox, he was inoculated with smallpox matter, but no disease followed. Several months later he was again inoculated with smallpox matter but again no disease followed.

(Jenner gave details of 23 cases in all before concluding) . . . 'that the cowpox protects the human constitution from the infection of the smallpox.'

Edward Jenner, *An enquiry into the cause and effects of Variola Vaccinae, known by the name of Cowpox*, 1798

❖ *It seems wrong today to attempt to give a boy smallpox. Why did it not seem wrong to Jenner?*

SOURCE 4 – Mankind can never forget you

Medicine has never before produced any single improvement of such utility. You have erased from the calendar of human afflictions one of the greatest. Mankind can never forget that you have lived. Future generations will know by history only that the loathsome smallpox has existed, and by you has been extirpated.

Thomas Jefferson, President of the USA, letter to Jenner, 1802

SOURCE 5

Cartoon, 1808, in support of vaccination. For a cartoon opposing it see page 39.

Overcoming smallpox

Jenner showed in 1798 that his technique worked, but this by itself did not mean that smallpox was overcome. The disease was to last for another 180 years. The graph on the right shows how the deaths from smallpox decreased in Britain.

There are no similar figures for the world as a whole, but the World Health Organisation estimates that in 1967 about two million people died from smallpox. It was in that year that they began a worldwide campaign to stamp out the disease. In 1980 WHO announced that there had been no cases anywhere for two years. The disease had been conquered completely.

❖ *Why did it take so long for vaccination to be fully effective?*
❖ *What other changes were needed first?*

Louis Pasteur finds other vaccines

After Jenner's discovery it was nearly 100 years before Louis Pasteur found a vaccine for another disease. Then there came several more in quick succession. Why did this happen then?

❖ *Why was there a delay of nearly 100 years between Jenner's first vaccination and these later ones. What other developments had to take place before Pasteur could succeed?*
❖ *What were Pasteur's motives in his work on vaccination?*
❖ *What factors influenced him or helped him to succeed?*
❖ *Were these factors so strong that the discoveries would have been made at about the same time even if Pasteur had never lived?*

It was in 1877 that Pasteur turned to the study that led to the discovery of new vaccines. At the age of 55 he was already a world-famous scientist. The best known of his many successes had been his clear proof in 1861–64 that air-borne germs may cause decay (see pages 42–44 and 105). But he had many other scientific achievements to his credit.

His successes were due partly to careful and exact observation, using the greatly improved microscopes that were developed in the early 19th century. They were also due to his outstanding skill in designing experiments to test his own and other people's theories. He was a man of great determination and energy. He had carried on even after a brain haemorrhage in 1868 that paralysed his left side. He enjoyed his success and his fame, and loved performing a decisive experiment in front of an audience.

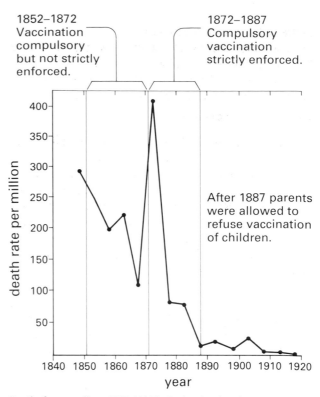

1852–1872 Vaccination compulsory but not strictly enforced.

1872–1887 Compulsory vaccination strictly enforced.

After 1887 parents were allowed to refuse vaccination of children.

Deaths from smallpox 1848–1920 in England and Wales

SOURCE 1

Pasteur in his laboratory

SOURCE 2 – Pasteur's motives

There is no greater delight for an investigator than to make new discoveries, but his pleasure is increased when he sees that they have a direct application to practical life.

Louis Pasteur, writing in 1865.

Pasteur was a great scientist and was inspired by the idea of science as a search for knowledge. But he was also anxious to make science useful to industry and agriculture. He had grown up in the Europe of the Industrial Revolution, with many new techniques coming into use in factory and farm. He was always ready to leave his laboratory and investigate on the spot and to show how well science and industry could work together.

In 1877, Pasteur took up the study of anthrax, a disease of sheep and cattle. This disease caused great problems for farmers throughout Europe. Once it caught hold little could be done. In one area of France it killed each year about 9 per cent of the sheep and 7 per cent of the cattle. Other French scientists had already done some work on the anthrax germ, so Pasteur, who had successfully solved so many of the problems caused by germs, decided to help with anthrax.

He had another reason for his choice. In 1876 the German doctor and scientist Robert Koch published his first discoveries – about the anthrax germ. Pasteur could not know how important would be the discoveries that Koch and his team in Berlin were to make over the next 20 years. But he did know that Germany was France's deadly rival.

In 1870 the German army had defeated the French, marched to Paris, seized part of France, and forced

SOURCE 3

France to pay Germany the sum of £200 million. France was burning for revenge, but knew that her army was far too weak. Pasteur, a patriotic Frenchman, could not help seeing the chance of scoring a scientific victory.

In 1877 he formed a team including vets and doctors and began a meticulous examination of the problem of anthrax. Their first aim was to work out in detail how the disease is transmitted. To do this they had to grow a culture of the germs and then inject them into animals in various strengths. In the course of this work they discovered in 1878 that a sheep which had recovered from the disease could not catch it a second time. Pasteur had always been interested in Jenner's work and in vaccination, and he saw at once how important this discovery was.

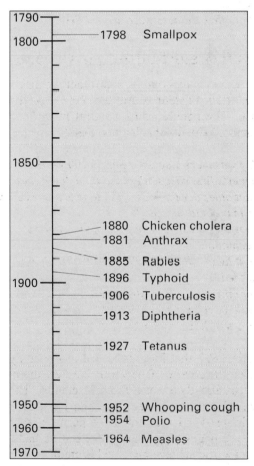

Year	Disease
1798	Smallpox
1880	Chicken cholera
1881	Anthrax
1885	Rabies
1896	Typhoid
1906	Tuberculosis
1913	Diphtheria
1927	Tetanus
1952	Whooping cough
1954	Polio
1964	Measles

Discovery of vaccinations

The battle of Sedan during the Franco-Prussian War.

Vaccination number two

While the work on anthrax was going on, Pasteur and his team were also asked to investigate chicken cholera. They were using chickens in their anthrax work, and the same technique of growing the germs and then injecting them in various strengths could be used.

One day in 1880, Charles Chamberland, a member of the team, happened by chance to use germs from an old culture that had been exposed to the air. He found that it did the chickens no harm. Pasteur was interested and asked him to try the same chickens again but with germs from a fresh culture. To check that this really worked it was also injected into some other birds. When these new birds died an agonising death, but the first group suffered no ill effects, Pasteur and Chamberland could see that they had hit on something important.

They carried out a further series of careful experiments which proved that exposing the germs to the air weakened them, and than an injection of the weakened germ protected the bird from the disease. They had found a second vaccination. Jenner had made up the word 'vaccination' from the Latin word 'vacca', meaning cow. Pasteur wanted to stress that his new technique was similar to Jenner's, so he used Jenner's word.

Vaccination number three

In 1881 Pasteur and his helpers went on to use the same method of weakening the germ by exposure to air to produce a vaccine against anthrax. When they were sure that it worked, Pasteur arranged the experiment described in Source 3. He invited a large audience of scientists, farmers, politicians and journalists, and his triumph was complete.

In Germany Koch tried out Pasteur's method, but failed to get similar results, so he wrote articles attacking Pasteur with some bitterness. But Pasteur was able to point out mistakes in Koch's work and to prove that he himself was right.

Perhaps the best proof was the effect on agriculture. Where Pasteur's vaccine was used the deaths from anthrax of sheep and cattle fell by over 90 per cent. One scientist worked out that the saving to French farmers was enough by itself to pay the £200 million to Germany.

Vaccination number four

Next, in 1882, Pasteur applied the same technique to rabies, the disease that drives dogs mad. The bite of a rabid dog can cause rabies in humans, and before 1885 this led almost certainly to a painful death. But rabies is a disease that develops slowly, and Pasteur hoped that the vaccine, if given soon after the bite, could prevent the rabies from developing. It was in 1885 that doctors in Pasteur's team used it to save the life of Joseph Meister. A fourth successful vaccine had been made.

SOURCE 1

Louis Pasteur vaccinating sheep against anthrax.

SOURCE 2 – Pasteur on Chance

In the field of observation, chance only favours those who are prepared.

Louis Pasteur in a lecture, 1854

SOURCE 3 – Anthrax can be prevented

Paris

June 2nd 1881

(by telegraph from our own correspondent)

Anthrax is a sickness which rages especially among sheep. It costs France several million francs a year.

M. Pasteur has separated the virus of anthrax and subjected it to chemical action. This has given it a graduated strength from the most harmless to the most virulent. He then set up the theory that by inoculating the virus at different strengths the animals might be protected from anthrax.

On 5th May, M. Rossignol's farm and 60 sheep were placed at M. Pasteur's disposal. Ten of the sheep were left untouched in order that they might later serve for a comparison. Of the remaining 50, 25 were marked with a hole in their ear and were inoculated on 5th May with weak virus and on 17th May with stronger virus. On 31st May none of them had lost fat or gaiety or appetite.

On 31 May the 50 sheep were taken and all inoculated with the strongest virus. M. Pasteur predicted that today, 2nd June, the 25 sheep not inoculated would be dead and that the inoculated animals would show no symptoms of sickness. Today at half past one a number of spectators came together to witness the results. At 2 o'clock, 23 of the sheep which had not been inoculated were dead. The 24th died at 3 o'clock and the 25th an hour later.

The 25 inoculated animals were sound and frolicked and gave signs of perfect health.

The agricultural public now knows that an infallible preventative exists against anthrax.

The Times, London, June 1881

SOURCE 4

Louis Pasteur and Joseph Lister being honoured by the University of Paris, at the Sorbonne in 1892.

4 THE MEDICAL RENAISSANCE

KEY QUESTIONS
◆ *How far did changes in ideas about other things change ideas in medicine?*
◆ *How did the coming of new techniques and new machines help the new ideas?*
◆ *How much was due to the work of individuals like Vesalius or Harvey?*

The changes that led to the scientific medicine of today were started in the 16th century by men like Vesalius and Harvey. In their lifetime, and for long afterwards, their new discoveries did not lead to new cures. When people did try a treatment based on the new scientific ideas it was just as likely to kill people as to cure them. This was the case, for instance, with the first blood transfusion (see pages 59 and 168–9).

As well as being uncertain, the work of dissecting and experimenting was often hard and unpleasant. It was likely to mean long hours working on corpses, which rapidly decayed. 'These things I have examined both in the hospital of St Bartholomew and in the Italian hospitals with much nausea and loathing and stench' wrote William Harvey in 1616.

So why did doctors in Europe in the 16th and 17th centuries take up scientific research of this sort and carry it on so successfully? Pages 142 to 151 suggest two particular reasons why this happened when it did, and tell the story of the two most important pioneers of scientific medicine, Vesalius and Harvey, in more detail than on pages 32 to 35. But all these things were parts of a wider and more important movement of ideas – the Renaissance.

The Renaissance : a 'wind of change'

The Renaissance started in Italy, mainly as a 'rebirth' of ideas and knowledge in art and literature. Once artists and writers had shown that new ways of working and thinking were exciting and successful, others followed suit. For instance, Columbus used new geographic ideas to plan a different route to China. Instead of reaching China he discovered a new continent, America, which became known as the 'New World'. The years 1500–1650 were a time when new thinking that seemed to turn the old ideas upside-down came to be accepted by more and more people. This was bound to change the attitudes of doctors and medical ideas.

The diagram on the next page shows some of the ways in which Renaissance ideas led to a revolution in doctors' understanding of the human body and of how it worked.

❖ *This cartoon suggests that the Renaissance started on one particular day. Is that true?*

Renaissance: new ideas

▼

Careful observation of nature

▼

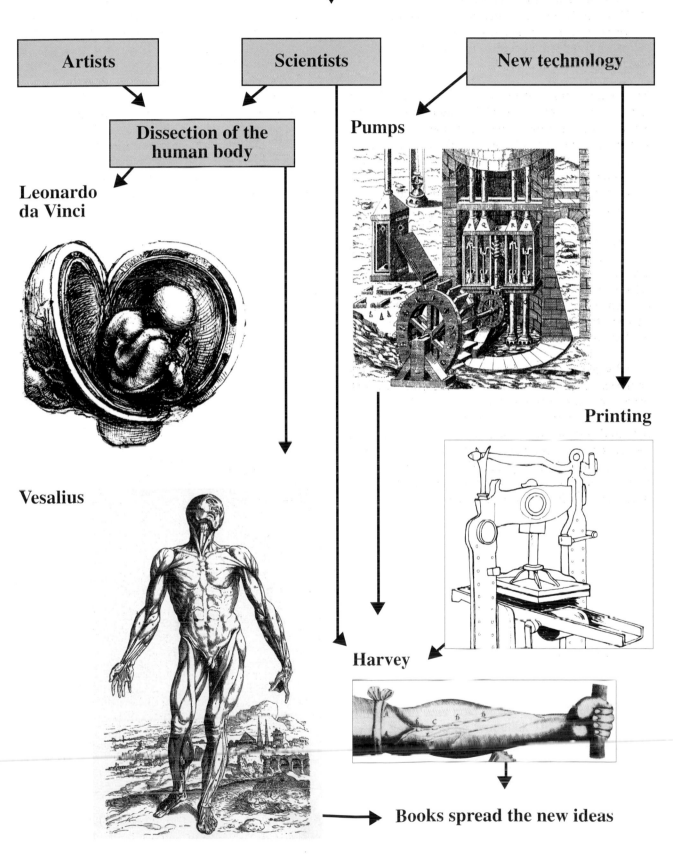

Artists

Scientists

New technology

Dissection of the human body

Pumps

Leonardo da Vinci

Printing

Vesalius

Harvey

Books spread the new ideas

Careful observation of nature

The writers and thinkers of 16th-century Europe were not in fact trying to put forward new ideas – they were trying to restore old ones. What they hoped for was to follow the ancient Greeks and the Romans. The ancient buildings or statues had been so beautiful, the poems and plays so fine, the scientific thinking so clear, that the Europeans were satisfied to accept the ancient standards. But in their effort to equal the ancients, the Europeans of the 16th century came across one ancient idea that had unexpected results.

Artists like Leonardo da Vinci (1452–1519) could see clearly that the sculpture of the Romans and Greeks was based on careful observation of nature. So they set out to do the same thing – to look carefully with their own eyes at the world around them and to draw or carve what they saw. To do this accurately you need to understand what you are drawing or carving, and this led them to study plants and animals in detail, and to study human anatomy. Leonardo carried out many dissections, and planned to make a full set of drawings of the human body, although he never completed it. He made a detailed study of the heart and lungs, and even proved to his own satisfaction that Galen's view of how they worked was wrong. He wrote about this only in his private notebook.

❖ *Could Leonardo's view that Galen was wrong have influenced Vesalius?*

Whether it did or did not do this, Leonardo's work and that of other artists did mean that by 1540, when Vesalius needed artists who could make really accurate drawings of every part of the body, he was able to find them.

SOURCE 1

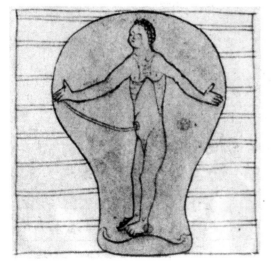

Drawing of a human foetus in the womb from a medieval textbook on midwifery.

SOURCE 2 – Painters need to know anatomy

The painter who has a knowledge of the sinews, muscles and tendons will know exactly in the movement of any limb which muscle by its swelling is the cause. So he will be able to show the various muscles in the different attitudes of his figures. He will not do like many who in different actions always make the same things appear in the arm, the back, the breast and the leg.

Notebooks, Leonardo da Vinci, before 1519

SOURCE 3 – You need 15 corpses

You will need three dissections in order to have a complete knowledge of the arteries, three others for the membranes, three for the nerves, muscles and ligaments, three for the bones and cartilages. Three must also be devoted to the female body, and in these there is a great mystery because of the womb and its foetus.

Notebooks, Leonardo da Vinci, before 1519

SOURCE 4

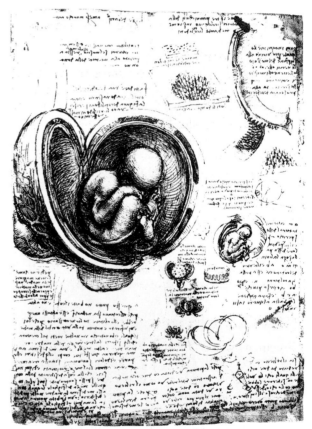

Drawing of a human foetus in the womb, from Leonardo da Vinci's notebook, c.1510.

Copernicus turns the sky inside-out

SOURCE 5

Before Copernicus.   A German woodcut of the 16th century.

Perhaps the most startling new idea of the 16th century was the new astronomy of Copernicus.

Before Copernicus

The ancient Greek view of the universe was that the Earth was in the middle, surrounded by the water of the oceans and the air of the sky. Higher still, the heavenly bodies, sun, moon, and planets circled in their orbits. Finally the whole universe, like an egg inside its shell, was contained inside a sphere to which the stars were fixed. The heavenly bodies were made of fire, so the whole theory fitted in neatly with the theory of the four elements: earth, water, air and fire. Other ideas like the theory of the four humours fitted in too, and for 2000 years details had been added to the system and calculations made based upon it. All the observations made by astronomers had been painstakingly fitted together.

After Copernicus

Copernicus was a Polish astronomer, trained in Italy about the year 1500, just at the time of the Renaissance. So he believed in careful observation, and was prepared to think for himself. Try as he could, he could not make his observations fit the ancient Greek theory. They might fit better, he suggested, into a completely new one. The sun might be in the middle of the universe, and the Earth just one of the planets circling round it. As well as being against ordinary common sense, this new theory would mean scrapping 2000 years of scientific thinking, and raising questions about many other ideas, including some parts of the Bible. It would certain cause trouble with the Church. Despite this

Copernicus wrote a book putting forward his theory, though he did not publish it until 1543, a few months before his death.

A bitter argument resulted and raged for over 100 years. For a long time the Catholic Church opposed the new theory and books teaching it were banned by the Church until after 1700. In the Protestant parts of Europe it was generally accepted much sooner – in England before 1600.

❖ *Would Copernicus' work be likely to encourage new ideas in medicine or to discourage them?*

SOURCE 6

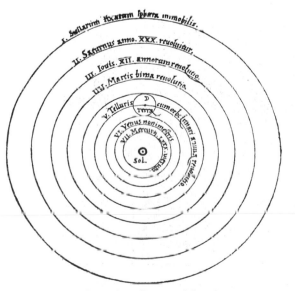

After Copernicus. Copernicus' diagram of the solar system. From *The Revolution of the Heavenly Spheres*, 1543.

Printing – a new technology

Printing with wooden blocks had been known in China 600 years earlier, but it was the coming of movable type cast from metal that made book production possible. This developed in Europe in the 1440s. By 1500, eight million books had been printed in Europe.

Before this it took weeks or months to make a single copy of a book by hand, so books were rare and expensive. Ideas were spread mainly by people travelling around talking and arguing, and this process might take years or even centuries. But with printing a few thousand copies of a book could be made in weeks. If it was written in Latin (and so could be read all over Europe) it could spread new ideas at great speed. Within a year or so of 1543, when Vesalius' *The Fabric of the Human Body* was published, every leading teacher of anatomy in Europe was able to see a copy, whether they agreed with Vesalius' ideas or not. The same was true of Harvey's *Motion of the Blood in Animals* of 1628. This book was reprinted in 1639, 1648, 1653 (in English), 1661 and 1671. By then nearly every educated person in Europe must have heard of Harvey's theory.

SOURCE 1

Part of the title page of Vesalius' book, *The Fabric of the Human Body*. Vesalius himself is shown on the left of the corpse in the middle of the picture.

SOURCE 2

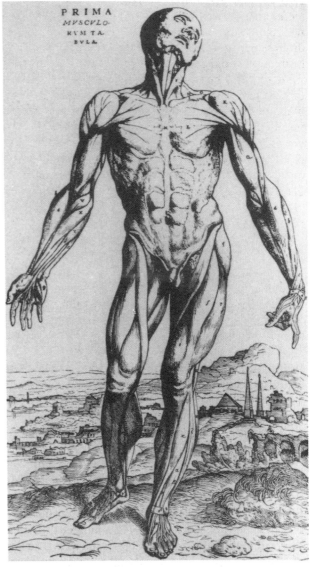

Drawing of the muscles from Vesalius' book, 1543. Each muscle is lettered for easy reference in the text.

For a subject like anatomy, pictures were as important as words. It was not until the Renaissance that artists like Leonardo da Vinci began to make careful and detailed drawings showing in proper perspective what things looked like. At the same time new methods of printing illustrations were developed. The drawings were carefully engraved onto blocks of wood or of copper and included in the pages of type. It was these illustrations, all carefully lettered to fit in with the text, that enabled Vesalius to show in exact detail what he had observed. Without the work of the artists and the inventions of printing and engraving his book would have been impossible.

❖ *How might the development of printing affect change in medical ideas?*

New technology – new explanations?

Europeans of the 16th century used many other new techniques as well as printing. They had water mills or wind mills in every village. They had pumps to drain water from mines or to supply it to towns. They had new designs of ships, new navigation instruments, new guns and new clocks. Skilled craftsmen of all kinds made and mended these machines and often made improvements in them. An intelligent young Englishman like William Harvey, growing up in the sea-faring town of Folkestone in the 1580s, was likely to be far more familiar with machines and how they worked than he could have been at any earlier period.

❖ *Could this have influenced the way Harvey thought about the working of the human body?*

The ancient writers like Galen did not look on the body in any way as a machine. It was made up of the four elements, each of which had its own natural way of acting, and each part of the body had its own nature, which caused it to act as it did.

William Harvey did not find this helpful. He spent years dissecting and experimenting with the hearts and blood vessels of animals and humans and trying hard to make sense of what he saw with his own eyes. What he did find useful and helpful was his knowledge of the simple machines that were so familiar in everyday life.

Harvey did not think that the body was a machine, but he found that thinking about machines helped him to explain it. Other scientists did the same. They found that if they assumed that the same sorts of explanations apply to the body as apply to machines they could begin to explain how the body worked. They have continued to do so ever since.

SOURCE 3

Armourer's workshop, c.1590. More people were now familiar with machines.

SOURCE 4 – The body is like a machine

A human body itself seems to be but an engine wherein almost all the actions are performed mechanically.

Robert Boyle, *The Usefulness of Natural Philosophy*, 1663

SOURCE 5 – Technology advances but science stands still.

For twice a thousand years the sciences have stood where they did, whereas in the mechanical arts which are founded on the light of experience we see the opposite. For they are constantly thriving and growing and at all times advancing.

Francis Bacon, *The Advancement of Learning*, 1604

SOURCE 6

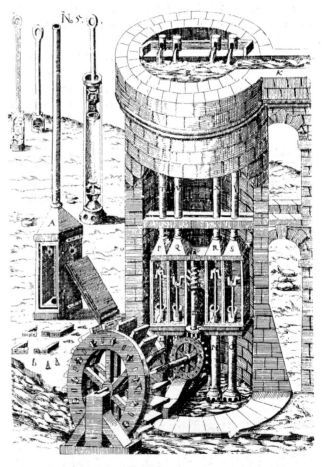

Water pump from F. Ramelli, *Various ingenious machines*, 1588. The separate drawings on the left show the valves.

SOURCE 7 – The heart behaves just like a water pump

When water is forced through pipes we can see and distinguish the individual compressions of the pump (perhaps at a considerable distance) in the flow of the escaping water. It is the same from the opening of a cut artery . . .

William Harvey, *On the Circulation of the Blood*, 1649

Scientific medicine: Andreas Vesalius

Vesalius' book *The Fabric of the Human Body* was the first really accurate description of the human body.

KEY QUESTION
◆ *Why was it written when it was?*

❖ *What factors helped Vesalius in his work?*
❖ *What was Vesalius' personal contribution?*
❖ *Were the other factors so strong that somebody else would probably have done similar work even if Vesalius had never lived?*

Vesalius was born in Brussels in 1514 and grew up at a time when the new ideas of the Renaissance were being widely discussed. His father was a doctor and this is probably why he decided to study medicine. He was so keen to gain personal experience of dissection that he stole parts of the body of a criminal from the gallows. The main medical textbooks were still Latin translations of Avicenna's Arabic version of Galen. But translations of Galen from the original Greek were now being made by Renaissance scholars. Jean Guinter of the University of Paris had made one of these, so at the age of nineteen Vesalius went to Paris to study under Guinter.

After three years in Paris the young Vesalius moved on to Padua in Italy, where he became professor of Anatomy in 1537. The University of Padua was one of the best in Europe, and the Town Council was keen to support it with money.

At this time the Pope and the Catholic Church were getting worried about the flood of new ideas and were just beginning a campaign to clamp down on dangerous ones. But Padua was part of the Republic of Venice, an area where there was much more freedom of thought than in other parts of Italy. So in Padua there was no difficulty in putting forward new ideas.

Here Vesalius spent six marvellous years of great achievement. The city law-courts provided the regular supply of corpses that he needed, and he had the freedom to design his anatomy course as he liked.

He relied a great deal on Guinter's excellent new translation of Galen, but he decided that what he also needed was a set of accurate drawings. A drawing could be much clearer and less messy than the real thing, and his students would know what to look for in the dissection. In Padua and in nearby Venice there were plenty of skilled artists ready to work under Vesalius' direction, so he had eight drawings made for his students.

SOURCE 1 – I am trying to bring anatomy back to life

In this fortunate age anatomy has begun to raise its head from the dark depths. I desired nothing more than the recovery of knowledge of the parts of the human body. So following the example of many distinguished men I decided to give what help I could. I decided that this branch of wisdom should be called back from the region of the dead. Even if it does not reach among us the perfection it had among the ancient teachers of dissection, at least I would be able to assert without shame that the modern science of anatomy is comparable with that of the ancients.

Andreas Vesalius, *The Fabric of the Human Body*, 1543

SOURCE 2

Andreas Vesalius at the age of 28, from *The Fabric of the Human Body*, 1543.

At this time the new techniques for printing pictures were just coming into use (see page 146). Vesalius decided to go on with the drawings and to make a complete 'atlas' of the human body. It was an enormous undertaking. Each part of the body might take many dissections before Vesalius could be certain of the correct structure. Then it had all to be explained and shown to an artist, and the book itself written and the pictures engraved. Vesalius was able to employ artists from the studio of the Venetian painter Titian. Finally it had to be sent across the Alps to Basle in Switzerland, where the best printing was done – no expense was spared on this remarkable and beautiful book. It is astonishing that the seven volumes were completed in the three years 1540–43.

As Vesalius worked, always comparing the structures he saw with Galen's book, he saw more and more clearly that Galen was wrong on many small points. Other people had already suggested that this might be so, but Vesalius was also able to show how Galen had gone wrong. Galen had relied mainly on the dissection of animals, assuming that the human body was similar. Often it was, but sometimes not.

SOURCE 3 – Could Galen be wrong?

The jaw of most animals is formed of two bones joined together at the apex of the chin. In man, however, the lower jaw is formed of a single bone. Nevertheless Galen and most of the skilled dissectors since the time of Hippocrates stated that the jaw is not a single bone. In spite of this, so far no human jaw has come to my attention constructed of two bones.

Andreas Vesalius, *The Fabric of the Human Body*, 1543

Most of Vesalius' anatomical ideas fitted in perfectly well with Galen, for whom Vesalius had very great respect. But in spite of this he really destroyed Galen's authority. Anybody with the necessary dissecting skill could check for themselves and see who was right, Vesalius or Galen. Vesalius was simply saying that the only real final authority had to be the actual evidence of the human body. Those who did check for themselves always found that Vesalius was right. His book can be looked on as the first real triumph of modern science.

This was difficult for many people to accept. Jean Guinter, Vesalius' old teacher in Paris, attacked him bitterly, and in some universities it was dangerous for the next fifty years or more to argue that Galen was wrong. But Vesalius' work was in fact so accurate and it was so easy to check this by a simple dissection, that go-ahead doctors and medical schools soon came to rely on it.

Vesalius took little part in the arguments. In a second edition of his book he wrote more openly about Galen's mistakes, but he took little further part in medical research. Perhaps as a result of his book he was offered a well-paid job as a doctor to the Emperor Charles V. He spent the rest of his life, until his death in 1564, in this honoured post.

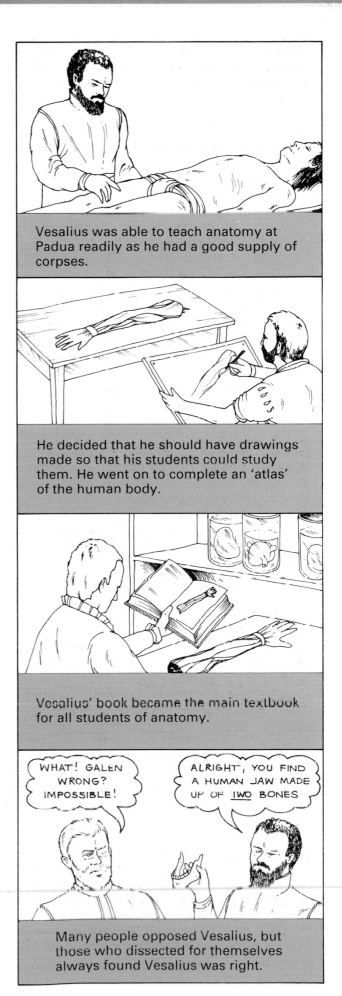

Vesalius was able to teach anatomy at Padua readily as he had a good supply of corpses.

He decided that he should have drawings made so that his students could study them. He went on to complete an 'atlas' of the human body.

Vesalius' book became the main textbook for all students of anatomy.

WHAT! GALEN WRONG? IMPOSSIBLE!

ALRIGHT, YOU FIND A HUMAN JAW MADE UP OF TWO BONES

Many people opposed Vesalius, but those who dissected for themselves always found Vesalius was right.

Scientific medicine: William Harvey

William Harvey's theory of the circulation of the blood was the first medical theory that was firmly based on scientific experiment.

KEY QUESTION
◆ *Why did it happen when it did?*

❖ *What factors helped Harvey to make this main discovery?*
❖ *What was Harvey's personal contribution?*
❖ *Were the other factors so strong that somebody else would probably have made the discovery even if Harvey had never lived?*

William Harvey was born in Folkestone, Kent, in 1578. At sixteen, the usual age to go to university at that time, he was sent to Cambridge. Perhaps he had already decided to be a doctor, because he chose a college where medical teaching, including the dissection of two corpses a year, had recently been established. Harvey spent six years there and then moved on to Padua to complete his studies.

At Padua his teacher was Fabricius, who was at the time writing his book on the valves in the veins. In his teaching he placed great stress on comparing the anatomy of humans with animals. Harvey was a good student and was awarded his doctorate in 1602.

On his return to England he settled in London and set up his own medical practice. He was very successful in his work. He became a fellow of the Royal College of Physicians in 1607, Physician in Charge of St Bartholomew's Hospital in 1609, and one of King James I's doctors in 1618.

At this time London was growing rapidly in size and wealth. Its citizens took a lively interest in new ideas. Explorers were bringing new plants from strange lands. New theories like that of Copernicus were widely discussed. There was a special interest in scientific ideas and in mathematics, on which many books were published. Public lectures were given and eagerly attended.

One regular set of lectures was given by the Royal College of Physicians on anatomy and in 1615 Harvey was appointed lecturer. Since settling in London he had probably carried on with some research and must often have argued things out with his friends, but now he had to prepare a series of lectures on every part of the body, with practical demonstrations and explanations of the sort that his London audience would understand. Over the next twelve years, as he wrote and delivered these lectures, he worked out his new theory and tested it in detail. By 1627 his mind was clear, and in 1628 he produced his great book.

SOURCE 1

The anatomical theatre built in 1594 at the University of Padua – a model reconstruction. The Padua medical school was so popular and famous at this time that this new theatre was built. It was designed so that 240 students could watch, none of them over seven metres from the dissection.

SOURCE 2

William Harvey aged about 55.

SOURCE 3 – A simple sum proves the theory

Let us assume the quantity of the blood which the left ventricle of the heart will contain when distended will be two ounces. In the dead body I have found it to hold over two ounces. Let us suppose that the fourth part of its contents are thrown into the artery at each contraction. This would give half an ounce propelled by the heart at each pulse. Now in the space of half an hour the heart will have made more than 1000 beats, in some as many as 4000. Multiplying then the amount propelled by the number of pulses we should have (at least) 500 ounces (14 kilos), a larger quantity than is contained in the whole body, a vastly greater amount than could possibly be supplied by the food consumed. In short the blood could be provided in no other way than by making a circuit and returning.

William Harvey, *On the Motion of the Blood*, 1628. Some of Harvey's figures here are wrong, but his argument is still valid.

SOURCE 4 – No other explanation is possible

I am obliged to conclude that in animals the blood is going round in a circuit with an unceasing circular sort of motion. This is an activity of the heart which is carried out by virtue of its pulsations, and that is the sole reason for the heart's pulsations.

It is difficult for anyone to explain in any other way than I have done the reason why all these things have been arranged in the manner I have described.

William Harvey, *On the Motion of the Blood,* 1628

Every part of the theory of the circulation of the blood was based on experiments that he had performed himself. Like Fabricius he dissected animals, sometimes living ones, to compare their anatomy with that of humans. For instance he used cold-blooded animals whose hearts beat very slowly, so he could watch the separate movement of the various muscles in the heart. He poked thin rods down veins to prove that valves only allowed one-way movement. He based other arguments on a careful consideration of the sizes of the various blood vessels. He measured the amount of blood in each heartbeat. He showed that a cut artery spurted in the same way as a pump spurted water. When he disagreed with earlier writers like Galen or with his old teacher Fabricius, he provided clear experimental evidence for his opinion. Like Vesalius he relied for proof on what he could see and show, so that other anatomists could always check it themselves by repeating the experiment. As well as being important in medicine his book is one of the foundation stones of modern science.

To many 17th-century doctors, the things William Harvey had seen as he dissected could not compare in importance with a system of thought built up over 2000 years by hundreds of great men from Hippocrates onwards. Books were written against Harvey, and it was over 50 years before his theory was fully accepted. But for those who understood his methods of proof, only one argument could work against him – the argument of experiment. And all the experiments, from that day to this, have confirmed that Harvey was right.

Harvey took little part in the arguments about his theory – it hardly seemed necessary. He continued as a fashionable doctor but he also made other discoveries, and in 1651 he published an important book on reproduction. Soon after that he retired from active work.

Harvey was educated in Padua, where he was taught anatomy by comparing humans and animals.

After his return to London, Harvey gave a series of lectures on the human body at the Royal College of Physicians.

Harvey experimented to show that his theory of circulation of blood was sound then wrote his book in 1628.

Many doctors refused to accept Harvey's theory, but those who repeated his experiments found he was right.

PATTERNS OF CHANGE

Understanding the pace of change

The first part of *Medicine Through Time* (pages 4 to 75) told the story of changes in medicine from the Stone Age to the present day. The second part (pages 76 to 151) looked at some of the factors which caused changes, and how they came together to make things happen when they did. This last part asks questions about the story as a whole.

Women in medicine, 1580

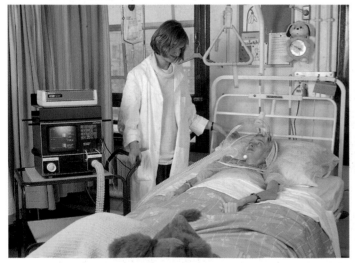

Women in medicine 1995

Lines of development

One part of this section (pages 156–157) discusses a 'line of development', clinical observation of the patient by the doctor, which has been important at all times but has changed greatly in the way it has been done. Using the index you could work out for yourself other lines of development, such as hospitals or doctors or the role of women in medicine.

Egyptian medical papyrus

Turning points

Events which caused sudden spurts of change, when development speeded up, are often called 'turning points' in history. Pages 158 to 165 provide evidence to help you to look for turning points in the struggle against malaria and in pharmacy. But why not also look for turning points in the history of medicine as a whole? The time chart on pages 154 to 155 may give you some clues about where to look.

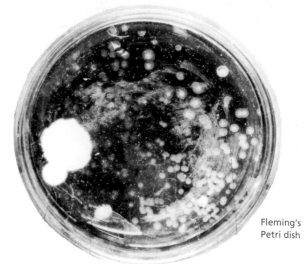

Fleming's Petri dish

Dead ends

Historians have to pick out those events which played a part in the story they are telling. Perhaps they sometimes only pick those that fit in with the interpretation they want to give. But history is about what actually happened, and not just what historians think. Pages 166–167 discuss some events which don't fit easily into neat lines of development.

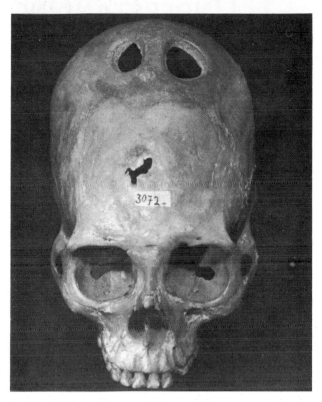

Trephined skull

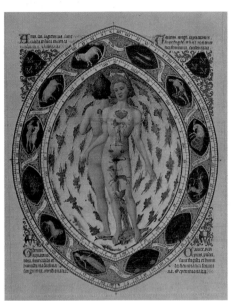

Astrological medicine book

Progress?

Probably the most obvious question about the story of medicine as a whole is 'Have things got better?' People often talk about 'progress' and assume that things get better steadily all the time. Is this true of medicine? Or have there been times when medicine has stayed the same for a long time – or actually got worse? These questions are looked at in more detail on pages 168 to 173.

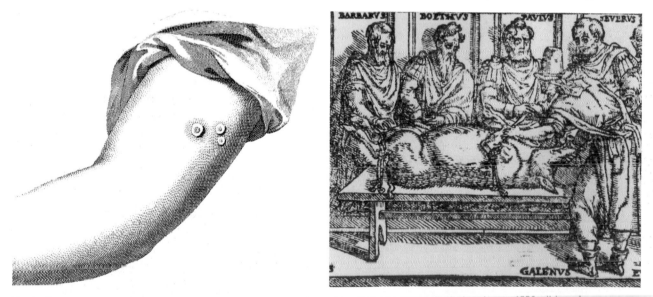

Vaccination

An illustration from a 1556 edition of Galen's book.

1 UNDERSTANDING THE PACE OF CHANGE

In the history of medicine there have been times of rapid change and other times when change has happened very slowly.

KEY QUESTIONS
◆ *What were the times of rapid change?*
◆ *What were the times of slow change?*
◆ *Can one period of rapid change be said to be more important than the others?*

❖ *There is only room on this time chart for a few of the main events in the history of medicine. You may think that other events should have been chosen instead, and this might have altered the pattern of change. Can you suggest other events that would make the pattern different?*

❖ *On a time chart like this it is easier to show changes than to show the things that stayed the same. What important things stayed the same for long periods?*

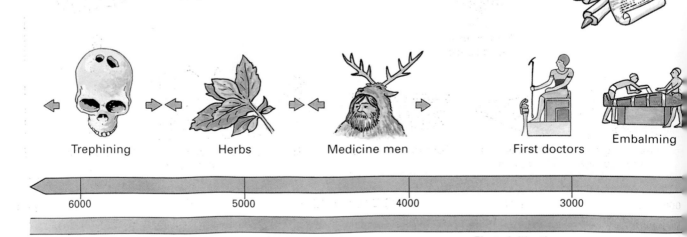

First medical books

Trephining   Herbs   Medicine men   First doctors   Embalming

6000   5000   4000   3000

First civilisation

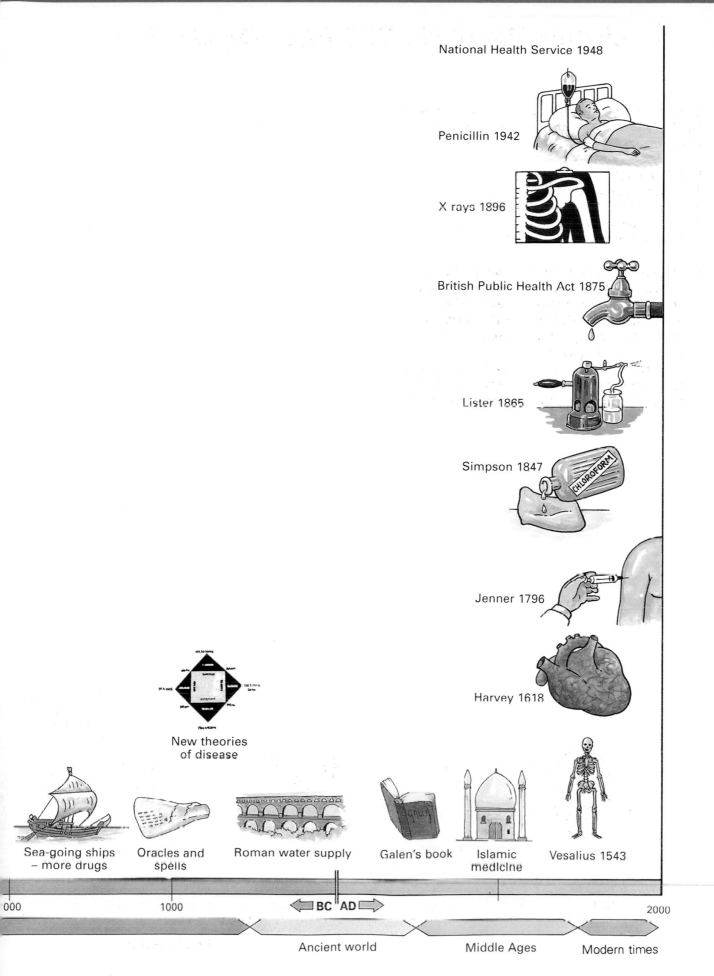

National Health Service 1948

Penicillin 1942

X rays 1896

British Public Health Act 1875

Lister 1865

Simpson 1847

Jenner 1796

Harvey 1618

New theories
of disease

Vesalius 1543

Sea-going ships
– more drugs

Oracles and
spells

Roman water supply

Galen's book

Islamic
medicine

2000

1000

1000

BC   AD

Ancient world

Middle Ages

Modern times

2 LINES OF DEVELOPMENT

KEY QUESTION

◆ *What medical techniques have developed continuously over long periods?*

Clinical observation through time

As you grow up you stay the same person but you get bigger and capable of doing many more things – you develop. It can be the same in history – a basic idea may stay the same although details change bit by bit as time goes on. For example the idea of careful observation by the doctor, usually at the bedside of his patient, has developed in many ways since the time of Hippocrates. But modern doctors would agree that they are still doing the same thing that Hippocrates was doing.

❖ *Look at Sources 1 to 8. How has clinical observation stayed the same? How has it changed and why?*

SOURCE 1 – Feeling the pulse?

If a doctor, priest of Sekhmet, or magician, places his hands or fingers on the back of the head, hands, stomach, arms or feet then he hears the heart. The heart speaks out of every limb.

Ebers Papyrus, c.150 BC, Egypt

SOURCE 2 – Look and ask questions

First of all the doctor should look at the patient's face. If he looks his usual self this is a good sign. If not, the following are bad signs – sharp nose, hollow eyes, cold ears, dry skin on the forehead, strange face colour such as green or black, red or lead coloured. If the face is like this at the beginning of the illness, the doctor must ask the patient if he has lost sleep or had diarrhoea, or has not eaten.

Hippocratic Collection, *On Forecasting Diseases*, 400BC

SOURCE 3

Doctor taking pulse, from a 13th-century Italian written copy of the *Canon of Medicine* by Ibn Sina.

SOURCE 4

Physician examining a patient, from *On Anatomy* by Guido de Vigevano, 1345.

SOURCE 5

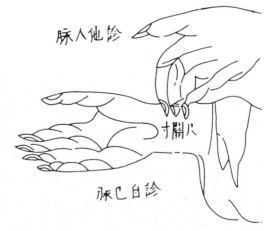

脈人他診

寸關尺

脈己自診

Chinese instructions for feeling the pulse. From San-ts'ai t'hu-hui, China, 1607. There are detailed instructions about feeling the pulse in *The Yellow Emperor's Classic on Internal Medicine*, 450-350 BC.

SOURCE 6

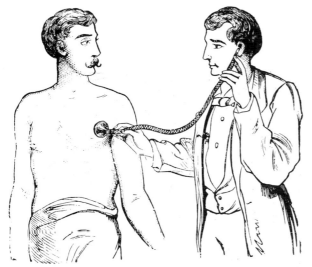

A stethoscope in use 1885. The flexible rubber tubes then available were more convenient than Laennec's wooden ones (Source 7). The double earpiece came still later.

SOURCE 7 – How the stethoscope was invented

(Laennec was trying to listen to the heart of a fat young woman)

Because of her stoutness I could gather little information by feeling with my hand or by tapping. The patient's age and sex did not permit me to use the kind of examination I have just described. (Putting his ear to her chest.) I remembered that if you place your ear to the end of a wooden beam the sound of a pin at the other end is most distinctly heard. Taking a sheet of paper I rolled it into a very tight roll. I placed one end of this over the heart whilst I placed my ear to the other. I was both surprised and gratified at being able to hear the beating of the heart with much greater clarity than I have ever done before.

René Laennec, France, 1816. Laennec went on to make wooden stethoscopes. The stethoscope quickly became the main way of examining the chests.

SOURCE 9

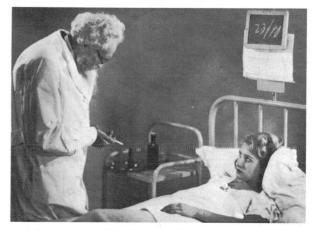

Clinical observation in the early 20th century (top) and in 1987 (bottom).

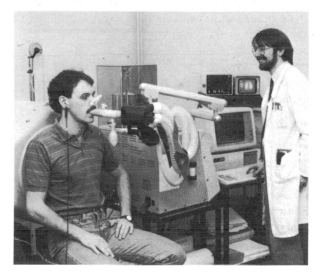

SOURCE 8

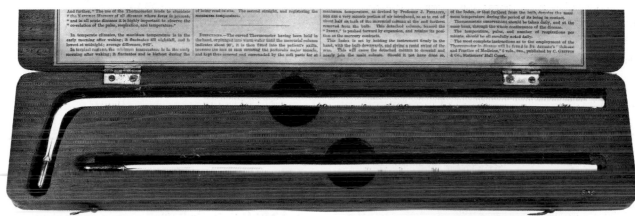

Clinical thermometer made about 1870. The thermometer was invented in the 17th century but not used in medicine until the 19th. Even then it took 20 minutes for one to register accurately. In 1852 a German doctor, Karl Wunderlich, began to record the temperature of his patients and showed how useful this was. In 1866 Thomas Albutt, a British doctor, invented this clinical thermometer, which gave an accurate reading in five minutes.

3 TURNING POINTS

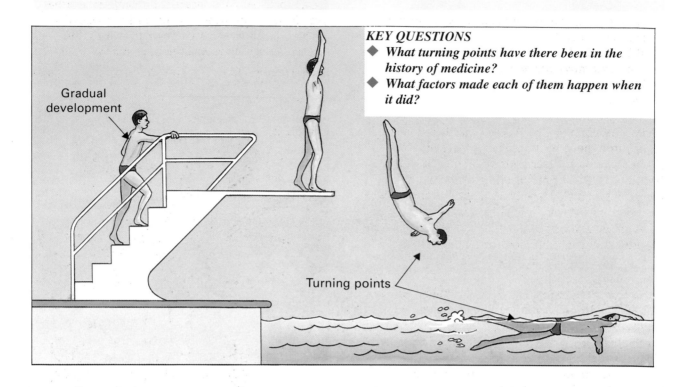

Gradual development

Turning points

KEY QUESTIONS
◆ *What turning points have there been in the history of medicine?*
◆ *What factors made each of them happen when it did?*

Some changes are so important that they can be called 'turning points' in history.

Going up the steps of the diving board is a bit like going through the stages of a line of development.

Each step adds a little until you are at the top. But then comes the turning point. Coming down is quite different! So is beginning to swim after the dive.

Pages 158 to 165 take two topics from the history of medicine as case studies, in which you can look for turning points and work out why they happened when they did.

CASE STUDY 1 The battle against malaria

MOUSTIQUES et MALARIA

CASE STUDY 2 Pharmacy through time

CASE STUDY 1 The battle against malaria

❖ *What turning points have there been in the battle against malaria?*
❖ *What gradual developments have there been?*
❖ *What has stayed the same?*
❖ *What factors helped to bring about the turning points?*

Malaria is possibly the disease that has done most harm throughout history. The symptoms are fairly clear, so we have descriptions dating back to at least 1000 BC. It hits people of all ages, and makes them sweat and then shiver uncontrollably. It comes back again and again, and gradually weakens people and stops them working. In 1955, 200 million people suffered and 2 million died from it, including 10 to 15 per cent of African children under four.

The name 'malaria' comes from the Italian for 'bad air'. The Romans knew by bitter experience that stagnant water and marshes that smelled bad in summer were places near which the disease was likely to strike. They drained several marshes near Rome, and could tell easily enough that this made the area healthier. But there was no way in which they could tell how the marshes with the 'bad air' caused the disease.

Malaria was once common in Britain, where it was known as 'ague', but it was far more serious in hot countries.

The first effective treatment was found by South American Indians, but there is no evidence to tell us when. By chewing the bark of the cinchona tree they could control the fever.

In the 16th century, Spain conquered most of South America and Spanish Jesuit priests brought the bark back to Europe. Here it was known as 'Jesuit's bark' and from about 1630 it was widely used against malaria.

Then in 1818 a French chemist was able to extract a chemical called quinine from the bark, and he showed that it was this that helped the victims of malaria. For nearly a hundred years it was the only known drug that could definitely be shown to control a disease. Without quinine the Europeans might not have been able to explore and conquer Africa.

SOURCE 1 – Marshes give off poisonous vapours

There should be no marshes near buildings, for marshes give off poisonous vapours during the hot period of the summer. At this time they give birth to animals with mischief-making stings which fly at us in thick swarms.

Columella, *Country Matters*, Rome c. AD 50

SOURCE 2

Mosquitoes biting, from *The Garden of Health*, 1491.

In the 1880s, Italian scientists following up the ideas of Pasteur and Koch discovered microscopic parasites in the blood of malaria victims. How did they get there? This question was finally answered in 1898 by Ronald Ross, a British doctor working in India. He showed that the parasite had to spend part of its life in the stomach of one particular type of mosquito. So if the mosquito could be controlled or killed, the disease could be prevented.

Long before this was known, the disease had died out in Britain. In the early 19th century, many low-lying areas had been drained and paved, including the banks of the Thames in London. It seems likely that this prevented so many mosquitoes from breeding and thus ended the disease.

After Ross's discovery it was proved in Cuba and the USA that by draining swamps the mosquitoes could be controlled and the disease checked. The same technique was used against other mosquito-borne diseases like yellow fever. But it was expensive and needed strong government organisation, so malaria remained a widespread disease.

This meant that quinine was a very important drug. It proved its worth by controlling malaria in the swamps and filth of the battlefields of the First World War. But the cinchona tree, which was the only source of quinine, will not grow in Europe. So in the 1920s and 1930s German scientists tried hard to make another chemical that would do the work of quinine. They wanted one that could be made out of cheaply available materials that Germany would not run out of in time of war.

In 1939 they succeeded in making 'chloroquin' – a man-made drug. Since then other 'synthetic' (or man-made) drugs have been developed to treat malaria.

SOURCE 2

Cartoon of Ronald Ross from a French paper, Mauritius, 1908. Ross is saying to the mosquito, 'You've had it chum! You can get lost!'

SOURCE 3

Standard Treatment For Malaria
(Chills and Fever)

Take 10 Grains of Quinine Sulphate by Mouth 3 Times a Day for 3 Days, Followed by 10 Grains Every night before retiring for 8 Weeks

FOR CHILDREN

Under 1 year, 1-2 grain	5, 6, 7, years 4 grains
1 year, 1 grain	8, 9, 10 years, 6 grains
2 years, 2 grains	11, 12, 13, 14, years, 8 grains
3-4 years, 3 grains	15 years or older 10 grains

SOUTH CAROLINA STATE BOARD OF HEALTH

Poster issued by the South Carolina State Board of Health in 1927, giving details of the standard treatment for malaria.

SOURCE 1

Ladies in a quarantine camp at El Tor, Arabia, in 1884. Many activities took place under mosquito netting.

SOURCE 4

Anti-malarial stamp, issued by Sierra Leone, West Africa, 1962.

SOURCE 5 – The disease is fighting back

Twenty years ago it looked as if the war against malaria had been won. But the disease is fighting back: there has been fourfold increase since the early 1970s. One reason is that the mosquitoes which transmit the infection in their bites are becoming resistant to the insecticides that once controlled them effectively. But more important is the emergence of malarial parasites resistant to existing drugs.

There is hope: a new drug from a herb called sweet wormwood, mentioned in a Chinese medical text more than 2000 years ago, could help to control them. Trials in China have shown that an extract of the herb, called qing hau sau or QHS is very effective.

Sunday Times, 18 August 1985

In 1939, chemists also discovered a new insecticide – DDT. This was cheap to make and could be sprayed on swamps or even inside people's houses to kill mosquitoes. In 1945, after the Second World War, it came into widespread use, and in 1955 the World Health Organisation announced a plan to wipe out malaria by destroying the mosquitoes everywhere. By 1965 it looked as if this was succeeding – there were only about 100 million sufferers and 1 million deaths.

Since then the mosquitoes and the parasites have struck back. A strain of parasite not affected by chloroquin has spread widely. So has a strain of mosquito not affected by DDT. In any case DDT has been found harmful to wildlife and perhaps to humans and its use is now strictly controlled.

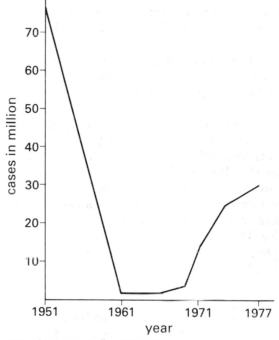

Cases of malaria in India, 1951-1977

CASE STUDY 2 Pharmacy through time

KEY QUESTIONS

◆ *What gradual long-term developments were there?*

◆ *What gradual long-term developments were there?*

◆ *What things (if any) stayed the same all or most of the time?*

◆ *What factors helped to bring about the turning points?*

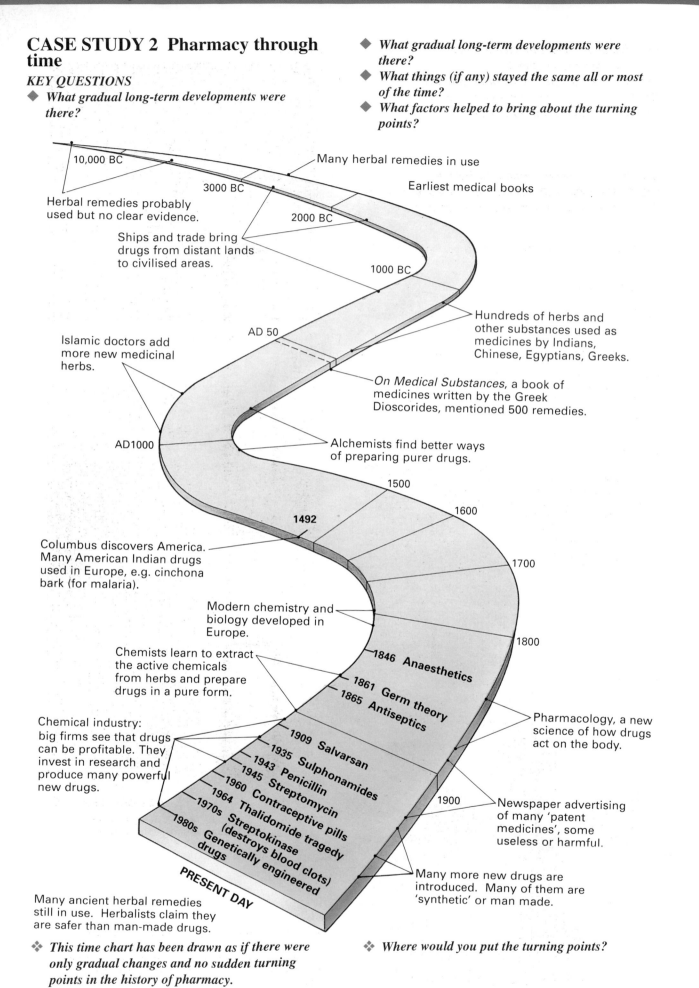

10,000 BC

Herbal remedies probably used but no clear evidence.

3000 BC

Ships and trade bring drugs from distant lands to civilised areas.

2000 BC

Many herbal remedies in use

Earliest medical books

1000 BC

Hundreds of herbs and other substances used as medicines by Indians, Chinese, Egyptians, Greeks.

AD 50

Islamic doctors add more new medicinal herbs.

On Medical Substances, a book of medicines written by the Greek Dioscorides, mentioned 500 remedies.

AD1000

Alchemists find better ways of preparing purer drugs.

1500

1600

1492

Columbus discovers America. Many American Indian drugs used in Europe, e.g. cinchona bark (for malaria).

1700

Modern chemistry and biology developed in Europe.

Chemists learn to extract the active chemicals from herbs and prepare drugs in a pure form.

1800

1846 Anaesthetics

1861 Germ theory

1865 Antiseptics

Pharmacology, a new science of how drugs act on the body.

Chemical industry: big firms see that drugs can be profitable. They invest in research and produce many powerful new drugs.

1909 Salvarsan

1935 Sulphonamides

1943 Penicillin

1945 Streptomycin

1960 Contraceptive pills

1964 Thalidomide tragedy

1970s Streptokinase (destroys blood clots)

1980s Genetically engineered drugs

1900

Newspaper advertising of many 'patent medicines', some useless or harmful.

PRESENT DAY

Many ancient herbal remedies still in use. Herbalists claim they are safer than man-made drugs.

Many more new drugs are introduced. Many of them are 'synthetic' or man made.

❖ *This time chart has been drawn as if there were only gradual changes and no sudden turning points in the history of pharmacy.*

❖ *Where would you put the turning points?*

❖ *What do sources 1 to 8 tell us about changes in pharmacy through time?*
❖ *Where do they show little or no change?*
❖ *Where do they show long-term development?*
❖ *Where do they show turning points?*

SOURCE 1 – A remedy when the belly is ill

Cumin ½ ro, goosefat 4 ro, are boiled, strained and taken.

Another remedy. Figs 4 ro, sebesten 4 ro, sweet beer 20 ro.

For a diseased eye

To clear up the pus – Honey, balm from Mecca and gum ammoniac.

To treat its discharge – Frankincense, myrrh, yellow ochre.

From the Ebers Papyrus, Egypt, c.1500 BC. A 'ro' – a measure; cumin – a herb; sebesten – a fruit; balm – the resin from a tree; gum ammoniac – the juice of a plant found in India and Africa.

SOURCE 2

Cure for stomach ache. Drawing of henbane from a 17th-century book of herbs. Henbane was used by the Egyptians against stomach pains. Modern chemists have discovered that it contains scopolamine, which numbs certain nerves.

SOURCE 3

SOURCE 4

Pharmacy in Baghdad, 13th century.

SOURCE 5

Pharmacy in Paris, 1624. Drugs made from plants from most parts of the world were available in Europe in the 17th century.

Black hellebore. From a copy in Arabic of Dioscorides' book, *On Medical Substances*, copy made in the 10th century. Original book c. AD 50. In other manuscripts black hellebore was recommended as a cure for insanity, epilepsy and arthritis.

SOURCE 6

From a book of herbs published in England in 1526. It claimed to give knowledge 'as practised by many expert and wise masters such as Avicenna' of all herbs 'which God has ordained for our welfare and health, for they heal all manner of diseases'.

SOURCE 7 – Tobacco can improve your health

Tobacco is found by good experience to help to spit out tough phlegm from the stomach, chest and lungs. The juice made into a syrup, or the smoke taken by a pipe helps to expel worms in the stomach and belly and the griping pains in the bowels. The seed is very effectual to expel the tooth ache, and the ashes of the burnt herb to cleanse the gums and make the teeth white. The juice is also used to kill lice in children's heads.

Nicholas Culpepper, *Complete Herbal*, 1653. This was one of many new herbals published in Europe at the time. They described thousands of medicinal plants, including the new American ones. Tobacco was not known to be a cause of cancer and other diseases until the 1950s.

SOURCE 8 – An old lady told him about it

William Withering, a Birmingham physician, described how he had learned about the effectiveness of the foxglove plant in the treatment of dropsy or swollen ankles, now known to be a major symptom of heart failure. Withering had learned about the usefulness of foxglove leaves from an old lady he had met on the way to Shropshire. The drug he described, known today as digitalis, is still one of the most important weapons in the treatment of heart disease.

It seems that foxglove had been known to be an effective treatment of dropsy for several centuries. Withering's contribution was to describe in some detail the dangers of the drug's misuse. He had no precise way of studying its full effect, but he was among the first to make as precise an assessment as possible of a drug's potential power.

V. Coleman, *The Story of Medicine*, 1985

Finding the first 'magic bullet'

Paul Ehrlich's team of scientists were trying to kill the germ of the disease syphilis inside the body. They infected rabbits with syphilis and then tried out a long series of chemicals. By 1909 they had tested over 600. Then Sahachiro Hata, a young Japanese assistant, found that the 606th compound worked.

SOURCE 1 – Tests repeated over and over again

Ehrlich looked at the records and said, 'No, surely not! It was all minutely tested by Dr R. and he found nothing. More than a year ago we laid aside 606 as worthless. You are sure that you are not mistaken, Dr Hata?'

Hata pointed to the records of the experiments, and said, 'I found that, Herr Direktor.'

'Then it must be repeated, dear Hata,' said Ehrlich.

The treatment with 606 had amazingly successful results, but Ehrlich demanded that it should be repeated over and over again with hundreds of experimentally infected animals. At length Ehrlich convinced himself of the outstanding curative power of 606.

'Always – 606 best,' said Hata.

'Incredible!' said Ehrlich, 'What an incapable good-for-nothing!' he exclaimed. Hata looked scared and stretched out his arms as if in defence.

Ehrlich put his hand on Hata's shoulder soothingly.

'Oh, not you,' he said, 'not you! No, the other fellow before you.'

Martha Marquardt, Ehrlich's secretary, Paul Ehrlich, 1949

❖ *Why were scientists of the early 20th century, like Ehrlich and Hata, so persistent and determined?*

SOURCE 2

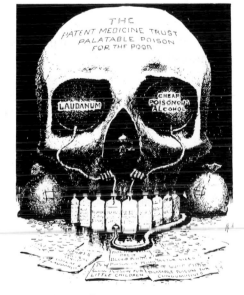

Cartoon from *Collier's Magazine*, USA, 1905.

SOURCE 3

British patent medicine advertisements, *Illustrated London News*, 1891.

SOURCE 4

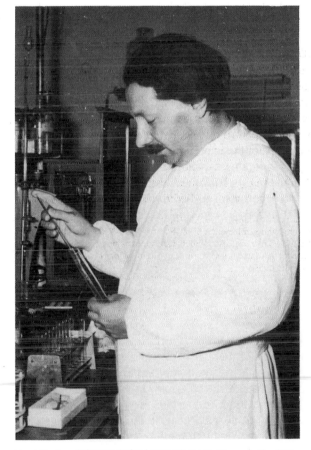

Ernst Chain, of Florey's Oxford research team. He made the first pure penicillin, 1940.

4 DEAD ENDS

KEY QUESTION

◆ *Have there been any changes in medicine that got nowhere, or at least not until long after their discovery?*

If you were finding your way through a maze you might often come to turnings that seemed to go in the right direction, but really led to dead ends. You might even go quite a long way down a turning before you found out if it was a dead end or not.

History is like a complicated maze. It is not just a series of success stories. When we look back we see the successes as important because they shaped what happened afterwards. For instance much of modern high-technology medicine followed from the work of Koch, who first identified and photographed the germs that cause some diseases.

But there were also many people whose ideas came to nothing, at any rate in their own lifetimes. There were other people whose ideas were widely accepted but then turned out to lead nowhere, like the dead ends in a maze.

❖ *Were any of the unsuccessful ideas shown on these pages completely 'dead ends'?*
❖ *What other examples of dead ends have there been in the history of medicine?*

We know that these ideas were unsuccessful at the time, because we know what happened afterwards.

❖ *How could people living at thetime tell whether an idea was a false turning or was likely to lead to a dead end?*
❖ *How can we tell which ideas that are new today are likely to lead to important developments and which to dead ends or false turnings?*
❖ *These ideas were unsuccessful. Does that mean that they have no importance for the historian?*

Ibn an-Nafis (1210–88) and the circulation of the blood

Ibn an-Nafis was an Islamic doctor who disagreed with Galen. Like Vesalius 300 years later, he could see no passage for blood through the septum of the heart (see diagram above). He said that the blood circulated from the heart through the arteries to the lungs and then back through the veins to the heart.

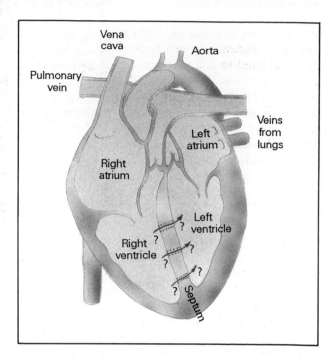

He wrote an account of his ideas, but as far as we can tell nobody followed them up, and Galen's view went on being the accepted one. In 1559 Realdo Columbo thought of the same idea for himself at the University of Padua. Harvey later studied at Padua and knew of Columbo's work. But Ibn an-Nafis' book was not rediscovered by historians until 1924.

SOURCE 1 – Galen thought there was a passage, but there isn't

When the blood has become thin it must be transferred to the left cavity. But there is no passage between the two cavities. The substance there is thick and impassable. It has no visible passage, and it does not contain an invisible passage which would permit the passage of blood as Galen thought. It must be, therefore, that when the blood has become thin it is passed to the lung in order to be dispersed inside the lung and to mix with the air. The finest parts of the blood are there strained, and pass into the vein and reach the left of the two cavities of the heart.

Ibn an-Nafis, Egypt, about AD 1242

All modern doctors would agree that Ibn an-Nafis was right. But there is no evidence that his idea was seen to be of any importance in his own lifetime or that it had any effect on later discoveries.

❖ *Does this mean that Ibn an-Nafis was of no importance in history?*

Franz Mesmer (1734–1815) and animal magnetism

Mesmer was an Austrian doctor who was interested in magnetism and attempted to use magnets to treat his patients. His treatments worked and he became very successful, but he then found that he could get the same effect just with his hands, using no magnets. So he developed the theory of 'animal magnetism', a special power that he claimed to be able to focus and control.

He was expelled from Austria as a quack, but was even more successful in Paris. The fashionable people there flocked to his consulting rooms, where he had a tub filled with iron filings. The patients gripped steel rods, and while Mesmer wore special robes and waved a wand, soft music was played. Many of the patients were cured or felt much better, and Mesmer became richer and more fashionable than before.

In 1784 the King set up a committee of leading scientists, including Benjamin Franklin and Antoine Lavoisier, to examine Mesmer's methods. They reported that there was no evidence for his theory, and that Mesmer's cures were produced by the imagination of the patients.

That was the end of Mesmer's fashionable practice, but he went on healing people and teaching his ideas. Others found that when patients were 'mesmerised' they could be persuaded not to feel pain. In the 1830s John Elliotson, the Professor of Medicine at London University, came to accept Mesmer's ideas. Other doctors were very suspicious. At this time doctors in Britain were keen to show that they were a respectable profession based on scientific knowledge. Mesmerism seemed more like witchcraft than science. So Elliotson was dismissed from his post. He went on to write a book *Surgical Operations in the Mesmeric State without Pain*, but within a few years chemical anaesthetics were discovered, and his ideas were not followed up. It looked as if mesmerism was a 'dead end'.

This was not entirely so, because later other doctors, mainly in France, studying mental patients, came to use some of Mesmer's methods. But they insisted that 'hypnosis' or 'suggestion' were nothing to do with 'animal magnetism' or with magic, but were parts of the normal behaviour of the human mind. Psychiatric doctors still use these methods today.

Franz Gall (1758–1828) and phrenology

Like Mesmer, Gall was an Austrian. He studied the anatomy of the brain and decided that each quality of a person's character was linked to one special part of the brain. If a characteristic was strong, then the person's skull had a bump over that area of the brain. So by feeling the bumps an expert could tell how a child might develop, or advise people about marriage. The ideas were widely accepted in the 19th century, and people brought charts of the bumps or porcelain models of the head so that they could do phrenology for themselves.

Gall made useful discoveries about the anatomy of the brain but after long argument his theory of the bumps was gradually shown to have no scientific basis. In the later 19th century research did show that different areas of the brain deal with different activities such as speech or hearing, but not with Gall's characteristics. By 1900 phrenology had fallen out of use.

SOURCE 2

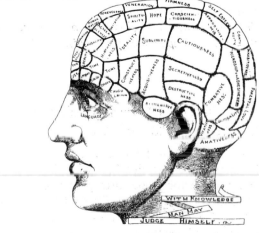

Phrenology chart.

5 PROGRESS?

KEY QUESTION
◆ *Have things always got better in medicine?*

People often talk about progress, meaning that they think things have improved or become more advanced. The opposite is regress, which means things getting worse or going backwards. Both these words assume that we all agree on what is 'good' and on which direction of movement is 'forward'. This is fairly easy if we are thinking of one particular line of development over a fixed period of time.

Step-by-step progress

Everybody would agree that doctors have advanced, or made progress, in anaesthetics in the last 200 years. The same is true of changes in their understanding of the blood in the last 400 years. The table shows how knowledge of the circulation of the blood and of how it operates in the body made no progress for a long time and then advanced greatly.

Knowledge about blood (see diagram on page 34)

Date	Name	Idea
AD 190	Galen	Blood moved in the veins and arteries, carrying 'spirits'. It passed through the septum.
1242	Ibn an-Nafis	Blood could not move through the septum, but circulated through the lungs instead.
1543	Vesalius	Blood could not move through the septum.
1559	Columbo	Showed how blood circulates through the lungs.
1579	Fabricius	Saw the valves in the arteries.
1628	Harvey	Full theory of circulation.
1661	Malpighi	Saw capillaries in the lungs.
1733	S. Hales	Measured blood pressure.
1800+	various	Structure and chemical composition of blood worked out.
1909	Landsteiner	Blood groups discovered.
1910+	various	Further knowledge of the complex chemistry of the blood and how it functions. Research continues, 'Haematology'

❖ *Could the later items in this table have happened without the earlier ones?*
❖ *Did more advanced knowledge of blood mean that doctors cured more patients?*
❖ *What other improvements in medical care were made possible by the progress in knowledge of the blood?*
❖ *What other examples are there in the history of medicine of step-by-step advance like this?*

SOURCE 1

17th-century woodcut of a blood transfusion from dog to man.

SOURCE 2

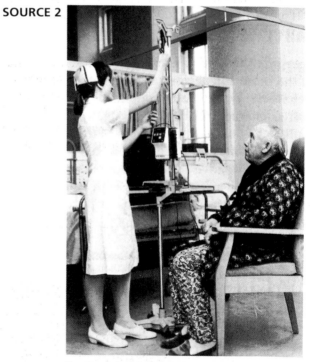

Blood transfusion being given today.

❖ *The methods of transfusion shown in Sources 1 and 2 are very different. Why has it been possible to develop safe methods of transfusion in the 20th century when it was impossible in the 17th century?*

Good in one way but bad in others?

Most changes can be looked at from different points of view. From one point of view they may be examples of progress – part of a step-by-step improvement. From another point of view they may be part of a harmful chain of events – examples of regress.

Two developments in surgery

Anaesthetics are one of the clearest examples of an improvement in the history of surgery. In Source 3, Simpson, the discoverer of chloroform, is trying to persuade people that this will be a great step forward. He refers to the work of Ambroise Paré, 300 years before, in developing an improved method of preventing bleeding during surgery. In fact Paré's method, though it saved the patient from violent pain, also made it more likely that wounds would be infected by germs on the surgeon's hands or on the silk threads he used to tie the arteries. This helps to explain why some surgeons went on using the cautery for so long after Paré's time. It was the development of antiseptic surgery by Lister after 1865 that made Paré's method really effective and important.

At first the coming of anaesthetics had a similar harmful effect. It encouraged surgeons to attempt more serious operations, such as the operation to remove the ovaries described on page 47. Until antiseptic surgery was developed by Lister after 1865 this probably led to more deaths than it prevented.

When we look back at the work of Paré, Simpson and Lister and see them as parts of the same story, we can see them as steps in the same example of progress. But before 1865 this was by no means clear.

❖ *Is it possible for people living at the time to be certain whether a new development is 'progress' or not?*

SOURCE 3 – People in the future will be horrified

Before Paré, surgeons had no other means of stemming the flow of blood after amputation than by scorching over the raw wound with a red hot iron or boiling pitch.

The suggestion of Ambroise Paré to shut up the bleeding vessels by tying them up with ligatures was a vast improvement. But the practice was new. The College of Physicians of Paris attacked Paré. They attempted to suppress the publication of his observations. For a century afterwards some of the hospital surgeons of Paris continued to prefer cauterising bleeding arteries.

Now we look back with sorrow at the pitiless practices of the opponents of Paré. In the course of years our successors will look back with similar feelings on many members of the profession at the present day. They will marvel at the idea of humane men confessing that they prefer operating on their patients in a waking instead of an anaesthetic state, and that the fearful agonies which they inflict should be endured and not avoided.

Sir James Simpson. Paper read to the Medico-Chirurgical Society, 1 December 1847.

❖ *Why does Simpson remind his listeners of Paré's problems 300 years earlier?*

SOURCE 4

Dr James Simpson and his friends after their first experiment with chloroform, 1847.

Good in one way but bad in others
The spread of high-technology medicine

A medical change that is taking place today is the spread of high-technology medicine developed in Europe and North America to the poorer countries of the world.

Some techniques like vaccination have already saved many lives. The successful stamping out of smallpox all over the world even saves money for the rich and poor countries alike (see Source 1). So there can be little argument that the spread of this method completes a story of improvement that was begun by Jenner.

Expensive hospitals and drugs, however, cost more than poor people in poor countries can afford. But these things come from rich and successful countries like Britain or the USA and have a high prestige. So the leading people in poor countries may prefer them to their own traditional healers and their low-cost remedies. It is also very profitable for the large drug-manufacturing countries in Europe and the USA to advertise and sell their products all over the world (see Source 5). These products can do harm as well as good, especially when used without proper safeguards.

High-technology medicine can have harmful effects even in the rich countries (see Source 2). In the poor ones it could destroy the traditional medical system and leave people worse off than before. The problem of how to spread its good effects without also doing very serious harm is one that remains to be solved (see Source 3).

SOURCE 1 – World is declared to be free of smallpox

A formal declaration that smallpox had been eradicated was made yesterday at the thirty-third World Health Assembly at Geneva.

A total of 3229 cases were notified in Somalia in 1977 but since 26 October of that year no further cases, other than a laboratory-associated outbreak in the United Kingdom, have come to light.

Two years without smallpox was considered necessary before a definitive declaration could be made, so in October last year triumphant officials recorded that the world was free of smallpox.

The Global Commission for the Certification of Smallpox Eradication presented its final report to the assembly yesterday, in which it gave the estimated cost of the eradication programme started in 1967. The total was put at $313m (about £137m) but the expected saving to affluent countries in discontinuing mass vaccination was put at $1200m.

The report points out that as recently as 1967 the disease was a major killer. In that year it was endemic in 33 countries, produced an estimated 10 million to 15 million cases and caused two million deaths.

The last laboratory-associated outbreak was in Birmingham in 1978.

Smallpox is thought to have first emerged in about 10,000 BC, and a suggestive rash on the mummy of Rameses V (1160 BC) [page 134] is consistent with such speculation. It was well established in Southern Europe by the 8th century AD.

Report by Annabel Ferriman, health services correspondent, in *The Times*, 9 May 1980.

SOURCE 2 – Doctors rely too much on drugs

Up to 5 per cent of patients admitted to hospital were probably suffering from a doctor-induced disease, claimed Dr Pietroni. 'We have 40 000 admissions a year for overdoses on psychotropic (mood-changing) drugs,' he said. 'The drugs bill for the NHS is £2 billion a year, more than is spent on the whole general practice service.'

The drug industry spends up to £5000 promoting its products to each GP each year. 'No wonder that some doctors assume that health care comes in the form of a pill.'

Report of statement by Dr P. Pietroni of St Mary's Hospital, London. He is chairman of the Holistic Medical Association, which opposes undue reliance on high-technology methods. *Guardian*, 2 July 1986.

SOURCE 3 – Use traditional healers

Less than 10 per cent of the Third World's three thousand million people live within walking distance of a modern health facility. For most of them the traditional healer, with his herbal treatments is their only contact with medicine of any kind. So it makes sense to use the skills of local people with their knowledge of local materials, rather than a limited network of high-tech facilities in the towns. In the words of Dr Ch'en Chieh, assistant director-general of the World Health Organisation: 'We now hope that developing countries will make better use of medicinal plants as a means to become self reliant. This is an appropriate health technology that fits in with the culture and natural resources of the country. It is also within the financial reach of impoverished millions.'

Guardian, 16 May 1985

SOURCE 4 – Expensive drugs, but her baby still died

As the boat drew in we heard a strange sound from the bank. A woman was crying. We found her with a dead baby in her arms and a collection of medicine bottles beside her. She had spent all her money on these expensive drugs. She could not understand how they had not saved her baby. This Bangladeshi woman had never been told what was obvious to the doctor who found her. The baby had become severely dehydrated from diarrhoea. Her death could have been prevented with a simple home-made solution of water, salt and sugar. No amount of medical care could have kept her alive.

D. Melrose, *Bitter Pills Medicine and the Third World Poor*, Oxfam, 1983

SOURCE 5

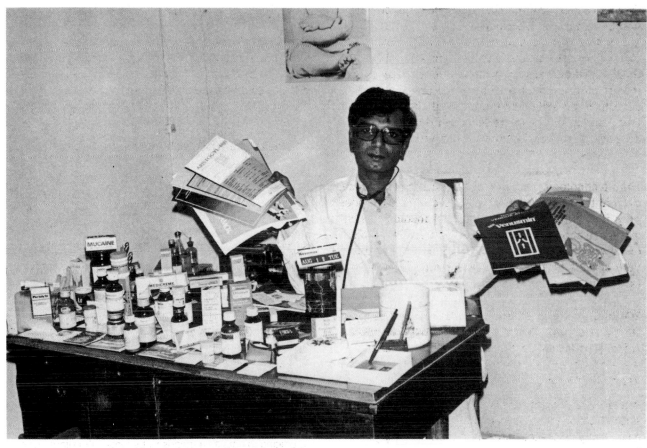

A doctor in Secunderabad, India, with the free samples of drugs and the leaflets about them sent to him by drug companies in two weeks, c.1980.

❖ *How could the introduction of modern European medicine have a harmful effect in the poorer parts of the world?*

❖ *Does this mean that it is an example of regress?*

Progress: a healthier life?

Instead of asking about progress in one line of development, like anaesthetics or knowledge of the blood, you might ask whether medical changes as a whole have made life healthier.

Sources 1, 2 and 3 provide evidence about how long people lived at various times and places.

❖ *What is the similarity between the 1841 graph (Source 2) and the part of the modern graph (Source 3) that deals wit the developing regions?*

Sources 4,5,6,7 and 8 deal with some of the causes of disease and death among children.

❖ *How might these be used to explain the differences between the graphs in Sources 2 and 3A?*
❖ *What other factors apart from medical improvements might help to explain the contrast between earlier periods and the 1980s, or between the two parts of the world today?*
❖ *Could these sources, or others from other parts of this book, be used to prove that the history of medicine as a whole is a story of progress?*

SOURCE 1 – Normal life-span 70–80 years

The days of our age are three-score years and ten, and though many be so strong that they come to four score years, yet is their strength but labour and sorrow. So soon it passeth away and we are gone.

Psalm 90, *The Bible*, c.900 BC

SOURCE 2

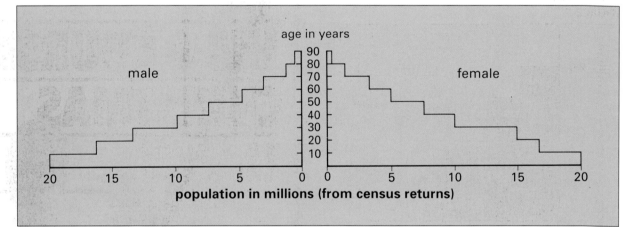

Graph of the population of England and Wales in 1841 by age and sex.

SOURCE 3

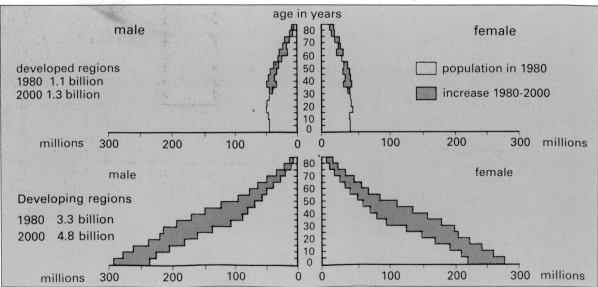

Graph of world population 1980 and (expected) 2000 by age and sex, in developed and developing regions. WHO, *World Health*, June 1984. The developed regions are the rich countries with an advanced technology and a high standard of living.

SOURCE 4

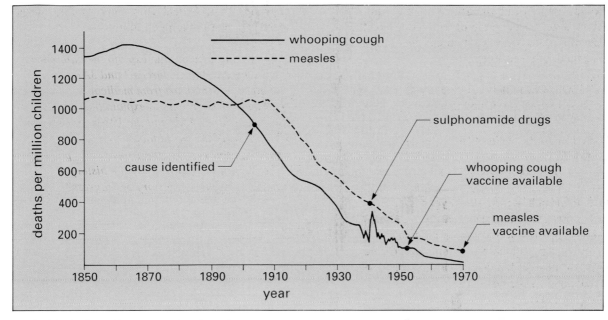

Graph of deaths from whooping cough and measles 1850–1970, England and Wales.

SOURCE 5

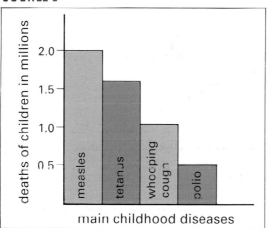

Graph of deaths from measles, tetanus, whooping cough and polio, 1983–84, in children in Third World countries. BBC TV, *Global Report*.

SOURCE 6 – Ten children die from diarrhoea every minute

The Expert Committee on Food Safety which met in Geneva this year noted that in 1980 there were 750–1000 million episodes of acute diarrhoea in children under five in the developing world. Nearly five million children died at a rate of ten every minute of every day.

WHO, *World Health*, October 1983

SOURCE 7 – How to save children's lives

The cost of full immunisation for each child would be $5 (£3.60). The cost of oral rehydration (salt and sugar mixture) for children with diarrhoea would be 5 cents (3.6p) per child. This would save seven million lives each year.

BBC TV, *Global Report*

SOURCE 8

HIS 4 COURSE CHRISTMAS LUNCH...

Hors d'oeuvre:...Grass
Main course:...Weeds
Dessert:............Berries
To Drink:..Dirty Water
And that's if he's lucky.

You can bring new hope to the hungry in Africa.

For example:

£11 provides all the special equipment needed to feed 13 particularly weak children in Ethiopia.

£30 provides the cement needed to deepen a well and provide life saving water for a village.

£80 provides food for the Ethiopian refugee children at the El Hawata camp in the Sudan for a day.

Advertisement, *Observer*, 23 December 1984, hunger in Africa.

Every effort has been made to contact the holders of copyright material but if any have been inadvertently overlooked, the publishers will be pleased to make the necessary arrangements at the first opportunity.

The publishers would like to thank the following for permission to reproduce photographs on these pages:

T = top, B = bottom, R = right, C = centre, L = left

Anthropological Institute, Florence 6R, 153TR
Barnaby's Picture Library 157 TR
Tim Beddow/Science Photo Library 62B
Bettman Archives 45
Bibliothèque Nationale, Paris 32L
Bodleian Library 41R, 144L, 163BL
British Library 79, 87TR
British Museum 10TL, 10TR, 11C, 24, 52TR
Cambridge University Library 28R
Centre for Development Education, Hyderabad 171
Churchhill Livingstone 42, 48, 55 (Pasteur), 76BR, 112BL, 115BC, 126TR, 138
Clarendon Press, Oxford 43TL, 87TR
e.t. archive 25B, 106TR
Edinburgh University Library 27
Mary Evans Picture Library 8R, 13, 53, 96T, 96B, 111TR, 127, 130, 132B, 158R, 165TR
Professor C.M.Fletcher 121TR, 121TL
Fotomas Index 147L
Stanley Gibbons 161
Glaxo 110C, 123C
Gonville and Caius College, Cambridge 156TR
Gustave Doré's *London* 50
Health Education Authority 73, 134R
Her Majesty the Queen 32TR, 143TL, 144R,
Herald and Weekly Times, Melbourne/Sir Stanley Baldwin 7
Hulton Deutsch Collection 43BL, 81L, 83B, 92R, 100T, 114C, 114B, 139, 141T, 167B, 168T
Imperial War Museum 97, 116
André Laubier 66

London School of Hygiene and Tropical Medicine 158L, 160TR
Lund Humphries 32BR, 113BR
Mansell Collection 8T, 14L, 20, 21, 31L, 49, 55, 62T (Nightingale and Simpson), 81T, 84R, 89, 90, 113TR, 129, 131, 132T, 141B, 156, 167T
Frederico Abora Mella, Milan 83TR
Museum of the History of Science, Oxford 119
National Library of Scotland 41BL
National Museum and Galleries on Merseyside, Liverpool Museum 76TL, 78BL, 112TL, 115TL, 126TL
Nobel Foundation, Stockholm 124
Oxfam 12R, 173
Photoresources 6L, 87L
The Photo Source 56R, 71, 113TL, 114T, 119L, 165BR,
Pictorial Press 70
Popperfoto 134B
Punch 94, 99T, 100B
Ann Ronan Picture Library 31R, 44, 46, 47, 55 (Jenner), 60TR, 111BR, 113BL, 136, 137T, 143TR, 145, 147, 153BL, 160CR, 160B
Royal College of Physicians 36TL, 55 (Koch and Harvey) 92L, 112T, 126TL, 150B,
Royal Infirmary, Edinburgh 60BR, 110B, 157CR, 168B
Royal Shrewsbury Hospital/Simon Fraser/Science Photo Library 111BL
St Bartholomew's Hospital/Science Photo Library 152BL
St Mary's Hospital, London 117R, 152BR
Science Photo Library 108BR, 109B
Sunderland Museum Collection 91
Syndication International 98, 99B
Geoff Tompkinson/Science Photo Library 109T
Topkapi Museum Istanbul 26, 163TR
UNICEF 71TR, 173
Victoria and Albert Museum 19CR, 28L, 80TL, 153TL
Wellcome Institute Library, London 10R, 14R, 17T, 17B, 22, 29L, 35, 36TRL, 39, 40, 41LT, 55 (Vesalius), 80TR, 83TL, 85, 89, 106, 107, 108CR, 111CR, 133, 137B, 143BR, 143BL, 146L, 146R 148, 150T, 152TL, 153BR, 157LT, 157B, 159, 163BR, 164, 169
World Health Organisation 68, 69
ZEFA 3

Published by Collins Educational
An imprint of HarperCollins*Publishers*
77-85 Fulham Palace Road
London W6 8JB

© HarperCollins*Publishers* 1996

First published in 1987 by Holmes McDougall Ltd, Edinburgh
This edition published in 1996 by Collins Educational

Reprinted 1996, 1997, 2001, 2002

ISBN 0 00 327007 6

Joe Scott and Christopher Culpin assert the moral right to be identified as the authors of this work.

Edited by Kate Woodhouse
Design by Sally Boothroyd
Production by Susan Cashin
Artwork by Raymond Turvey, John Booth, Nancy Bryce, Steve Gibson, Denby Designs, Harry Trowell, David Wilson.
Printed in Hong Kong

www.**Collins**Education.com
On-line support for schools and colleges